SOUL MEDICINE

Medical Challenges on Life's Uncertain Journey

John E. Postley, M.D.

The Love and Logic
PRESS Inc.
Golden, Colorado

To Elaine
Partner and Muse

ISBN 0-944634-33-8

Library of Congress Cataloging-in-Publication Data
Postley, John E.
    Soul medicine : medical challenges on life's uncertain journey /
by John E. Postley.
      p.   cm.
    ISBN 0-944634-33-8
    1. Critical care—Decision making. 2. Critically ill—Family relationships
I. Title.
RC86.7.P675 1995
616'.028—dc20   95-24224
                                           CIP

Text Editor: Adryan Russ
Designer: Bob Schram
Cover Designer: Barry Eisenach

Printed in the United States of America

Table of Contents

Preface

Serious illness is an unwelcome visitor who steals into each of our lives and affects our families and our friends. Whether or not we are careful in leading our lives, but especially if we are reckless, we cannot escape its visit. We have little choice about when it will strike. It will likely choose a moment when we are most eagerly planning to do something else. Our surprise will be mixed with anger and disappointment.

We can confront this visitor badly or well. If badly, we may lose forever the chance to set our own goals. If, however, we understand those issues with which we are faced we can make real choices so that, even if things turn for the worse, we can be satisfied that our choices were our own and that we gave comfort where we could.

The medical issues with which I will deal are not the latest CAT Scans, MRIs or genetic engineering. As our technology continues to become ever more sophisticated, it often isolates the patient from human support when it is most needed. The family stands apart unable to communicate needs or provide comfort as the patient becomes an appendage of the ICU. The medical issues I discuss deal with the suffering of men, women and children as patients or as families of patients.

My greatest concern has been trying to understand human response to critical illness. What does it mean to the patient, to the family and to the doctor? How often are everyone's needs compatible? How often at odds? What are the forces in modern medicine that promote or prevent communication? How did we get to this point? Where will it lead? What have some doctors done to protect their own families from this? What can you do to ensure that you and your family can support each other when the time comes?

Every person and every family is unique. There is no script which will be right for everyone. However, I hope that this book will provide enough questions and examples, both positive and negative, to help each of you find the proper structure to support you when you need it.

The first chapter describes my own experience during my mother's final illness—how my feelings evolved as I realized how sick she really was—and how all of us worked together to make her final months a true reflection of her values. The intensity of these personal trials has forged my professional experience into a more profound understanding of the ordeals that confront other families.

The following chapters will develop your ability for medical decision-making. They are designed to help you understand the issues and how to elicit the information you need from the professionals who are helping you. A discussion of goals that are possible in serious disease leads to advice about establishing those goals which will most completely embody your values.

After choosing your initial goals, you will have to constantly evaluate their continuing relevance. The clinical stories demonstrate that as illness evolves, goals will change. Sometimes this happens quickly but, more often, slowly. Examples of each type of evolution will allow you to see how others have coped with these problems. Finally, when cure is no longer possible and life is winding down, concrete victories over pain and suffering continue to inspire us to do our best.

What that best may be and how to communicate it to our families becomes a most urgent concern. Learning how to promote these ends challenges our ability to find hope when circumstances seem most desperate.

The physician plays a key role in these events. What qualities to look for in a physician and how to elicit them when you need to is woven through several chapters. There is help in structuring your family's relationship with the physician. A chapter looks at how illness affects the relationships of family members—the connected angles of the medical communication triangle: patient, family and physician.

Another chapter is devoted to examining the distortion of family communication resulting from serious estrangement. A plan is offered for resolving the pain by repairing the relationship. The emotionally critical concerns of fear and grief are treated, each in its own chapter. Organized programs are discussed to reduce these cosmic terrors to human scale.

Living Wills are mentioned often in the press but many people are unsure about what they are or how they feel about them. A full discussion describing the difference between Living Wills and Health Care Proxies (Durable Powers of Attorney), as well as the issues you must understand to protect yourself, occupies another chapter. The associated problem of choosing among home, hospice, nursing home or hospital as a place to receive care is also discussed, as well as making the level and kind of treatment relevant to the patient's goals.

Sometimes the visit of serious illness affects a friend's family. What can you do to be helpful? What should you avoid doing even if you think it is right? Getting over the awkwardness in being helpful is not difficult once you know how.

How do you protect life when illness strikes and extend it in the face of illness? How do you preserve the quality of that life as you confront the challenges of illness? And finally, how do you savor with your family the fulfillment of that life as it winds down? This is not a book about death. It is a book about life—how to achieve the life we want and live it as we see fit until our final moments.

CHAPTER ONE

Death
and Birth

I love you very much. You and Patsy have made me so proud." The words were quiet, the breathing noisy as the white-haired woman lapsed into a coma, again. My sister and I held each other as we cried. Our mother's struggle was almost over. A few hours later when her breathing stopped forever and the tears had finally subsided, we could begin to reflect on the year we had been through.

Noted for Longevity

"John, I have just examined your mother's eyes and she has some unusual crystals in her cornea. I have never seen crystals quite like this before but they are described in myeloma (a kind of bone marrow cancer)." This phone call from her ophthalmologist was the first clue that my mother's vigor was not unlimited. She was 87 and her vision was failing yet she insisted on driving herself from her house in Connecticut to New York every Monday to "go to the office."

With the implications of the ophthalmologist's diagnosis overtaking my thoughts, I had to leave my office. I take care of many of my friends, and many patients I have cared for have become friends. Taking care of final illness in people in whom you have an emotional investment is painful. Usually, I have enough lead time from diagnosis to deterioration to be able to work through my own grief before having to help others. Part of that process involves anticipating the needs of both patient and family, being the familiar guide in unfamiliar territory. Now I was to be the guide and the guided.

My mother had had remarkably few medical needs during her life. She came from a family noted for longevity. We would often joke that they were too mean to die. Furthermore, my mother's habits were ideal to express that longevity. She didn't smoke, rarely drank alcohol and despite being a wonderful cook would feast on a bowl of rice, skim milk and fruit if she were alone. She kept her weight down out of vanity and was physically active because there was so much she wanted to do. She thought taking an aspirin and a calcium pill was a lot of medicine. She didn't see a doctor regularly because she felt fine, and when she didn't she would ask me what I thought. Not a perfect situation but one that had worked for her.

The diagnosis of myeloma presented several problems. My mother did not fear death. She spoke occasionally about her feeling that losing control of her mind or home was more to be feared than death. But for many people of my mother's vintage, any cancer was worse than death. They feared the pain, the loneliness, the sapping of funds they had spent so long to accumulate. There was a stigma attached to this unspoken disease—a stigma that I did not understand and still don't. But it was common, and to have told my mother that she had any kind of cancer would have destroyed her desire to live and amplified the pain she was to have. However, my relationship with Mother was built on truth and trust as well as love. If at all possible I couldn't and wouldn't lie.

"I spoke with Dr. Donn about your examination today. He said you have some crystals in your cornea and that's why your vision has been getting worse. If we can find out what the crystals are made of, we may be able to make them go away."

"I told you there was something the matter with my eyes," she said. "It wasn't normal that I shouldn't see better. How long will it take before I can see well again?"

"Well, we have to see what exactly is causing this before we can start talking about treating it. You are going to need several tests but I don't think you will have go into the hospital. I've made an appointment for you to see Dr. Carter tomorrow."

Delighted that there might be something remediable dimming her vision, my mother underwent the x-rays, injections, barium enema and GI series and even the bone marrow examination with good humor and impatience. "That bone marrow test was painful. But when are you going to stop doing all this testing and start giving me something so that I can see better?"

"Mother, you have to wait. Dr. Carter has to get all the results and then decide what to give you. These medicines can be very strong and may have severe side effects. You really don't want to get started with the wrong one."

Dr. Carter started her gently on an oral chemotherapy regimen that would have few immediate bad effects, and her crystals resorbed at a faster rate than any one would have predicted. Unfortunately, her bone marrow also responded faster than anyone predicted and she soon developed large bruise marks all over her body from a profound drop in her platelet count, one of the clotting factors in her blood. The medicine was stopped but the drop continued and her red blood cell count went down as well. This was more important to her since it made her very short of breath when she tried to walk from her apartment door to the elevator.

Not feeling strong enough to leave her apartment building, Mother became depressed. She agreed that although her vision was better and she could see more clearly to drive, she really was weaker and she would have to let someone drive her out to the house in the country where she could rest to regain her strength. Dr. Carter left our university for another and I chose Dr. Hyman, one of my most respected professors, to take his place. He agreed that I could take Mother up to the country but if she did not show a change for the better soon, he recommended that she be hospitalized for a transfusion.

The idea of being hospitalized did not appeal to Mother at all. She loved hospitals but only as places where she could volunteer to help others. The loss of control and helplessness that being a patient in a hospital implied were anathema to her. However, she was getting so weak that she agreed. But, she got Dr. Hyman to arrange an outpatient transfusion so that she could go back home if she felt as strong as she hoped she would.

The day I took Mother for her transfusion, I was very scared. She was so weak, I wanted to carry her to the car but she insisted on walking herself, very, very slowly. At the hospital, she agreed to use a wheelchair, reluctantly. Things moved efficiently. The pre-transfusion blood tests were taken, Dr. Hyman came by to see that there were no new problems and then the transfusion began. With the nurses fluttering about, Mother relaxed in the lounge chair with the perfect positive faith that she would feel fine soon—and she did. It had been an exhausting day but she was happy to be back in her own bed that night.

When the blood count continued to rise on its own, the question of resuming chemotherapy came up. Mother was quite clear that she had no intention of continuing to take that medicine—the one that had caused bruising and low blood count. However, her vision continued to deteriorate and she wanted to try something that might help. Dr. Hyman suggested a cortisone derivative but this had side effects of its own. She had taken it briefly when her platelet count was low, so we knew she would not get high blood pressure or diabetes, but she could still have an ulcer or most probably develop osteoporosis and spinal fractures. On the other hand, it was likely to help her vision and might retard some spinal problems by dissolving the tumors in the marrow. Both Dr. Hyman and I went over these issues with her, in detail, several times, mostly for ourselves. Mother was feeling stronger and she wanted better vision again. She certainly had an intimate knowledge of the bad effects of medicine, but she thought that Dr. Hyman would pick a better drug than Dr. Carter had, so she was eager to press ahead.

The next couple of months went pretty smoothly. The medicine helped her vision. She had some moderate back pains which lasted a day or two and then subsided. I was lulled into the hope that this could go on forever. Maybe we had over-treated her at first and the side effects had been avoidable. Alas, this was wishful thinking. Despite the low-level cortisone, her vision slowly began to deteriorate again and she became impatient to regain her earlier condition. The medicine was increased with anxious trepidation. Then the bottom fell out.

"Oh, Johnny, I couldn't get out of bed today. My back hurt so much, I had to crawl to the bathroom last night." I called Mother after my office hours to see if she had returned from her office so that I might drop by for a visit on my way home. I rushed over and let myself in with my key. I found mother contorted in her bed supported by pillows, barely moving. I kissed her hurriedly and set about probing the areas that hurt. It was immediately clear that she had suffered a compression fracture of a vertebra in her lower back. The combination of the cortisone and myeloma had weakened her bones so much that this one gave way just by being subjected to the weight of her body.

That my mother hadn't called in the morning to tell anyone she was in pain was quite typical. One part was stoicism, but in an earlier day, there might have been a silent rebuke for my not having called to see how she was. However, since Mother had developed the myeloma, I called and spoke to her every day and visited a couple times a week, either alone or with Elaine or Johnny, my wife and son. Today, Mother was not indulging in any games. She had been in too much pain to move and hadn't had any food or water all day. There seemed no point in telephoning her doctor at this hour. I wanted time to think and Mother needed some nourishment.

Dr. Hyman and I agreed that the cortisone had to be dropped to the most minimal level in view of this side effect. When confronted with the alternatives, my mother concurred that even her vision was not worth the pain from the fractured vertebra. Within a week the pain began to subside and Mother was moving around more. She felt strong enough to go back to the country where her life resumed its normal cadence.

A Lesser Level of Functioning

Margaret, my mother's housekeeper for the previous 30 years, was more frightened than my mother. Margaret was 84 years old, my mother 87. They had been the constantly bickering odd couple since my father's death 25 years before. In those last months, Margaret often took me aside and asked me what was the matter with my mother and was she dying. I had told her what I had told my mother: Mother had a bad protein in her blood, it was affecting her vision, and the medicines that could help it were very strong and had side effects we were trying to overcome. With respect to Mother's dying, she was hardly a young woman and while anything might happen at any time, I certainly did not anticipate anything now. My confident voice was more important than my words in soothing Margaret's fears. She didn't want to know the truth, she just wanted her friend to be well enough to complain again.

My mother's last months were not simply the descent of a long successful life into a valley of pain and loss. Had there not been objective high points, she would have created them. But she was able to derive great delight from participating both physically and vicariously in the events around her.

Mother mostly recovered from that vertebral fracture. The pain came and went but often stayed, and she was more and more reluctant to leave her apartment. Occasionally, if she felt strong enough, I would drive her to my home for dinner, but more usually I would drop by and help fix something for her to eat. Elaine would often join me and we would have a drink while Mother ate. We would talk about the past and the future. Mother was a great planner and it was easy for her to speak of times "after she was gone." Elaine had taken over as my mother's lawyer and their relationship, aside from being loving, was very seriously professional. Their mutual compulsion for tidiness meant that Mother's affairs were always in order. As her time came closer, she would go over with Elaine the allocation of her possessions, but this still seemed sufficiently distant to her. She was more concerned with the dreams and achievements of her children and grandchildren.

There was a gradual transition over the months from full functioning to the limited life that Mother eventually accepted. She refused to give in until a medical emergency (anemia, vertebral fracture pain, weakness) left no choice. Then, once the emergency was resolved, she accepted the lesser level of functioning as at least an improvement from the depth of the crisis. This stepped decline allowed her to see even reduced function as a victory.

Increasing weakness led to another transfusion session at the hospital and although she felt stronger afterward, the more persistent pain discouraged her. She told me that she had had enough transfusions and wasn't going to have any more. At this point pain relief became a greater problem. Reluctant to accept any mental clouding as the price for pain relief, she continued to use aspirin until it produced a severe stomach upset. Dr. Hyman had prescribed a strong narcotic for her to have in reserve if the pain became more severe, but the one time she took even a half, she felt so dizzy that she vowed never to take it again.

The increasing weakness, the refusal to have more transfusions, the increasing pain and immobility described a sharper slope to Mother's downward course. Yet a few days later when Elaine and I went out to visit, she was in good spirits, delighted by the profusion of spring flowers that she could enjoy from her sofa in the den. We had a quiet weekend together. After she took another fall producing another vertebral fracture, I called my sister and told her to plan a trip back to see Mom soon. She was expected the next weekend and I now thought that she could probably postpone it. Elaine and I returned to New York with a sense of reprieve.

The reprieve was short-lived. Monday, Mother sounded weaker on the phone but claimed that she had just come back from a trip to the bedroom and needed to catch her breath. She did not sound much stronger when I called an hour later. Tuesday was about the same; no worse but no better. I began to think that this was our final countdown. When I called Wednesday morning, Mother sounded a little stronger but she had developed a cough. I rushed through the day. That afternoon some friends had planned a special party to celebrate the second printing of my book. I had told Mother I would call her after the party to report how things had gone, but I really expected to head out to the country as soon as I could.

The first guests arrived as my beeper went off. As I called my service, I feared what the response might be. There was an urgent call from my mother's nurse in Connecticut. I called to find that she had developed a slight fever, only 100, but I knew it represented a significant change in her course. I told them we would be there in two hours. Some of my closest friends knew how sick Mother was but most did not. I didn't think this was the time to tell them and I went back to greeting the rest of the guests. When Johnny and Elaine arrived, I told them to eat plenty of hors d'oeuvres because we were going to drive up to Connecticut right away.

As soon as I got in the car, I called my sister in California. She was scheduled to arrive on Saturday but I was beginning to believe that might not be soon enough. I told her to drive to the airport and get the first plane heading to New York and then have her husband call us with the flight number so we could send a car for her. Even if I were wrong about the imminence of death, our mother was obviously sick enough that she would want to be there. My sister is a nurse and this was a time that her help would be greater than mine.

The drive to the country was uneventful and we got there sooner than expected. Mother was reclining on the sofa, coughing, mildly feverish and very weak.

"Oh, Johnny, what is going to happen? How long is this going to last?"

I kissed her and sat in the chair beside her. I took her hand and stroked it softly. A burning in my throat muted me, almost. Finally, I regained my speech. "Don't worry, Mother. You are almost at the end. I think this is your last illness. That protein is causing a reaction in your lung which leads to pneumonia. We can give you lots of antibiotics and oxygen but I don't think it will change anything. What do you want me to do?"

"I don't want anymore medicine. That I know! But how long is this going to take? When is Patsy coming?"

"I called her while we were driving out. She's getting a plane and will be here tonight. Ted will call with the flight number so we can get her. I don't know how long this will last. You are still pretty strong. It could be a few days. It could be a few weeks. No one can really tell for sure. I think we can handle anything here and you can have any medicine you need. If you want anything different, let me know and we can arrange it."

"No, I would rather stay here. Anna is very good to me, but I worry about Margaret. I don't know if she can take it."

My sister arrived about 2 a.m., worried and exhausted. By that time Mom had gone off to sleep, breathing more quietly, and her temperature had come down to normal. It almost looked like another false alarm. I talked with my sister for a while and brought her up to date. I told her what medicines we had and what more I would have the pharmacy send over in the morning. Then I gathered the rest of my dozing family and headed back to New York for clean clothes and to clear my office so that I could go back there to stay for the coming Memorial Day weekend.

Preparing for the End

My first call the next morning was to my medical school roommate who practiced orthopedics in the town in which my mother lived. It was becoming clear that Mother would die very soon and I needed to be sure that a local physician would be available to provide a death certificate. And if at the last moment Mother decided that she wanted to be in the hospital, some other physician would have to do that. I was grateful for the backup. The emotional burden was growing. I had been through this many times before but never with my mother. I was glad that there would be an out if something unexpected occurred.

I finished seeing my early morning patients and sped back to the country. By the time I arrived, my sister had organized the household tightly. I went over Mother's condition with Pat, asked her if there was anything else she needed and then went into Mom's bedroom to be with her. She was uncomfortable from the back pain and the increasing cough but she didn't want to take any medicine. She ate a little applesauce and drank some water but mostly she seemed content to sit with one of us holding her hand, just being close. Now and then she would want to talk. She wanted to be sure that we knew what she wanted done with her things. She spoke about her grandchildren and her hopes for their future. She gave us advice about financial decisions she thought we should make.

Listening to Mother at this time provoked an astonishing revelation. She knew she was dying; we had discussed it in just those terms. She had reiterated her wishes about disposing of her property and was entirely consistent in her instructions from one day to the next. Her thoughts were clearly expressed and she was not taking any medicine which would alter her thinking. Yet, it was as if she had two entirely different mind sets and that she could switch between them.

One moment she would be discussing who got which silver service and the next she would be wondering about a decision that could not be made for six months, long after she knew she would not be alive. When I had seen this before in others, I had assumed that it was a confusion due to the severity of illness or the effect of mind-altering medication. The clarity of her logic in each state belied any confusion. It was a simple demonstration of the complexity of the human mind relating to its environment. This realization has helped me understand apparent contradictions in others' behavior, in both patients and their families. Some are genuinely confused; others are not. To mistake this behavior for confusion not only disparages the speaker but robs us of the opportunity to appreciate the complexity of human intelligence.

The next two days passed slowly. Knowing that there were no replays, we savored every moment. Mother had made her plans, said her good-byes and was impatient to move to the next stage. Pat and I respected her values and wishes but did not want our terrible loss to occur any more quickly than it had to. Each day Mother would insist on making the trip from the bedroom to the den twice. Once in the morning after being washed and then in the afternoon after a nap. It was difficult to watch. The slow struggle, shortness of breath and pain from the spinal fractures were all part of Mother's statement that she hadn't given in. She knew the inevitable and welcomed it, but it would have to overtake her. She had no intention of changing her life's pattern now.

Emotionally overwhelmed by my impending loss, I looked to any concrete task as a respite from staring into the abyss. As Pat and I tried to support Mother, Elaine and Johnny supported us. Their tender concern during these dark hours made it possible for us to carry on. Each had an important role in this time of crisis and the whole was clearly greater than the sum of its parts. The unity of our pain bound us even more closely together as a family.

Through Friday night, Mother became clearly weaker. The cough was deeper and it was a greater effort for her to talk. For the first time Saturday morning, she did not insist on getting out of bed. She took a little water and coffee and applesauce. Then she whispered, "Johnny, it really hurts. Can I have one of those pain pills now?" Pat crushed the pill so that Mom could swallow it in her weakened state. We both held her as we helped her take the water to swallow the pill and then gently put her down. She was quiet for a few moments and then in a whispered voice told us how much she loved us and how proud we had made her. Those were her last words. She went off to sleep and lapsed into a coma an hour later. By evening she had stopped breathing.

Honoring Mother's Wishes

The scenes of mother's last year have played over and over again in my mind. The intense grief was always tempered with a great feeling of accomplishment. My father's only charge when he had died 25 years before had been to take care of my mother. This seemed pretty silly to me at the time since it was clear that, at least financially, my mother was going to be taking care of me for some time to come. But as I got older, I realized what he meant. He had seen his parents and my mother's parents die—some well, others not so well. He had seen what it was like to be alone or dependent on others. He did not want that for his wife.

My mother was always outspoken about her principles and values. She needed to think and work and contribute. If she couldn't do those things, she was not interested in remaining on earth. She would just as soon be put on one of those ice floes, like the old Eskimos, and drift off to sea. She had made it quite clear long before living wills and health care proxies, that if I ever allowed anyone to hook her up to one of those breathing machines, she would haunt me forever. My greatest fear as she grew older was that something unpredicted would happen and she would end up in a hospital with just the treatment that she abhorred and no way to reverse it. This had almost happened five years before when she had been run down in the street by a rushing taxi and ended up in the emergency room of one of our city hospitals. The arrogant young doctor in charge of the emergency room was not inclined to accede to my requests to release my mother so that I could take her uptown to my own hospital and, in fact, he had called the hospital police to eject me before cooler heads prevailed.

Mother had survived both the shattered leg and the emergency room but I had had the fright of both fearing that she would die and fearing that I would not be in a position to honor her wishes. As we all lived mother's last year, I continued to be struck by how lucky we had been. At each crisis, the necessary resources were at hand. Whether it was a housekeeper or nurse or driver or dinner, each seemed to be waiting in the wings for the cue to appear.

I began to wonder about the strain on others going through similar trials. The uncertainty of diagnosis and the course of treatment, unsure how the condition would evolve and what complications to prepare for, not knowing when and if to call the doctor. All these worries magnify the pain of losing a parent. I had helped many families but never with the intense appreciation of the strain that exists in every quarter. How did the others do it? My explanations of disease and predictions of complications could never have the immediacy to patients' families that they had for a repeat caretaker like me. I know that many families agonized over calling me when they needed to, just as other families called too often. I could not spend as much time as they needed or I wanted, and I knew few resources to call upon outside the hospital. I had been able to rely on my family for both emotional and physical help. We lived in the same city as Mother. What would have happened if we had lived on another coast? What if I were a single parent and not able to leave my office whenever I had needed to? What if I did not have a wife on whose judgment I could rely when I faltered?

These are the questions triggered by mother's death that gave birth to the idea for this book. It was then that I decided I had to attempt to help others find solutions to such questions.

CHAPTER TWO

A Structure for Thinking

Cascading emotions can easily overwhelm us as serious illness develops. Whether for ourselves or our families, fear of pain and uncertainty about the future quickly erodes our ability to confront problems. This cloud of fear must be dispersed. We need to think clearly about the issues of sickness and treatment. What are they, and how can we understand them so that our choices reflect our real values and wishes?

Developing Your Strategy

For physicians as well as patients, creating a strategy to approach these issues keeps us from ending up where we don't want to be. With a structure for thinking that we can follow, we can proceed with confidence to our conclusion. Here are some steps to begin your strategy.

Gather information. Gathering information is always the first step. What medical decisions need to be made? What are the facts? What are the possibilities? Where do you get the information you need about this particular illness? How much can you rely on it? How do you check it? Information gathering is a crucial first step on this journey.

Establish your goals. What are the possible treatments? The possible outcomes? How will they affect you? What outcome do you prefer, and how can you get there?

Set your path—the road you will take. The point of thinking about the nature of the particular illness and the possibilities of treatment is to establish your choice of treatment options, and then act on them.

Create alternatives. As the results of treatment choice become evident—illness evolves and complications can develop—you may find that your goals will change. Selecting secondary goals as alternatives will allow you to keep control of your direction.

If all goes well, you will need only these four steps. If curative treatment fails, however, there is a fifth step.

Find hope in the midst of medical retreat. As life ebbs, relieving today's pain is more important than regretting the loss of yesterday's cure.

Gathering Information

To properly establish your strategy, you will need to begin by collecting information regarding your particular medical situation:

✦ **Diagnose the illness.** A diagnosis is a technical term for the name of the illness. A condition cannot be treated until it is named.

✦ **Establish the certainty of diagnosis**. Since many diagnoses are "guestimates" based on incomplete information, gathering all the information you can get is essential.

✦ **Examine the cause of the condition.** Before you begin steps to treat the condition, you will want to know, as fully as possible, what may have caused it.

✦ **Examine treatment possibilities.** What are the treatment possiblities? How can they affect the illness? In the absence of treatment, what might happen? If treatment begins, what might happen?

This is going to take a great deal of effort on your part. Get a notebook to write down what you have learned. Date your entries. Write down the names of the people with whom you speak. This notebook will act as an important reminder to you but also a place to write the questions which you will want to ask the doctors.

What Is the Name of This Condition?

The initial job in dealing with a medical situation is to define as precisely as possible what that situation is. The words "cancer" and "heart attack" strike fear in most people, conjuring up pictures of wasted patients in severe pain or red-faced men gasping for breath. And yet these words are so general that they can be applied to many ordinary, trivial conditions. Even defining a cancer further as "skin cancer" can be confusing. It may refer to a very limited malignancy with no chance of distant spread even with great delay in treatment, or to a very aggressive and fatal malignancy that has spread irreparably by the time of diagnosis.

To be in a position to make a decision you will need more than merely a short name for an illness. On the other hand, a long name written in medical jargon or Latin will not be much more helpful. All these names are a kind of shorthand that doctors and nurses use. Do not accept them as a definition of an illness even if they sound somewhat familiar. Don't be afraid to ask an important question you may want to put at the top of your list: "What does that mean?"

An illness can be an injury such as a broken hip, or an infection such as pneumonia, or a tumor, malignant or benign. Malignant tumors (another name for cancer) generally grow progressively and have the capacity to spread to distant areas where they may destroy vital structures. Benign tumors (*not* cancerous) usually grow only locally, in the place where they arise. While benign tumors are most often much less dangerous than malignant ones, a critically placed benign meningioma of the brain is far more worrisome than a malignant basal cell carcinoma of the back. One may grow to strangle vital structures in the brain while the other may grow for a long time nowhere near a vital structure. There are, also, other more unusual

kinds of illnesses: tissue inflammations of allergic or uncertain causes, toxins which can get into food or water and congenital abnormalities both anatomic and biochemical.

The point is that there are many kinds of illnesses and many
causes for them—too many for me to describe here for you and too
many for you to learn in a crash course in diagnosis. The fundamental source of information is likely to be the doctor who has
made the diagnosis. You have to learn how to question your doctor
so that you can begin to get the facts you need.

While the first question should be "What is the name of this
condition?" the next needs to be, "What does that mean is wrong?"
Don't be afraid to say, "I don't understand. Can you explain it again
in simpler words?"

**Before you can proceed, you must have some understanding
of what the physician believes is the problem.**

After you have this information, you can go on to the question
of how the doctor arrived at this diagnosis and how certain it may
be. What tests or what physical findings support the diagnosis? Are
there other possible diagnoses?

While this approach is equally valid in common illness as in
complicated disease, do not expect a physician to go into a long discourse on the variety of lung responses to infection if you go in for
treatment of a cough productive of yellow sputum following a case
of the "common cold." This is surely an instance of bacterial bronchitis and the explanation that the cold weakened your resistance to
a bacteria which set up the infection should be adequate. This is a
very common development and blood tests, chest x-rays or CAT
scans are not necessary in an uncomplicated case.

The insistence on complicated tests for common illness does
not improve treatment nor make it more scientific if the history and
physical examination are consistent. They make no more sense than
using an "18 wheeler" to deliver a carton of eggs from the super-
market. It will work but it doesn't deliver the goods any faster or

any better. However, if the case is complicated by failure to respond to treatment, or fever or pre-existent lung disease, then further testing and explanation may well be necessary.

An essential factor in keeping simple things simple and still not delaying a timely diagnosis in more complicated conditions is "follow-up." This is a responsibility of both patient and physician.

If the treatment of an illness is not proceeding as expected,
the patient must let the physician know,
and the physician must be available to learn the information.

If instead of your cough resolving, you develop fever and chest pain, your physician should be notified. This may be relatively easy if you are being treated by a family doctor who knows you. It may be almost impossible if you had been treated in an emergency room without much continuity of care. Even for the most simple of illnesses, you should be given some expectation of outcome, so that you will know when to contact the doctor if you are not better. Asking "When can I expect to feel better?" is not being pushy. It is being a responsible participant in your own health care.

So, the first ingredient in learning to make a medical decision is finding out what the doctor thinks you have. Not surprisingly, the doctor is going to be your primary source of information in this regard. If the illness does not seem too serious, you are likely to leave it at that. If you fear that the situation is more worrisome, you will want to get some independent information.

Medical encyclopedias and on-line computer PDQ databases are excellent sources. There are patient-oriented medical encyclopedias available in libraries and bookstores. Columbia University has a particularly good one, but there are others.

If the medical diagnosis is a cancer, you may want to go on-line, if you have computer experience or know someone who does. Some public libraries can be helpful. The PDQ database should definitely be consulted. PDQ is a collection of on-line information about treatment options for many types of cancers. The information includes standard and experimental treatments and lists doctors who may be doing special research in each area. It is the creation of Richard Block (the "R" of H&R Block) who was frustated by his inability to get answers when he developed cancer many years ago. His survival and the survival of a great many people who have used the PDQ database are due to the active role they have taken in their own illnesses.

A poor source of information in serious illness is the friend whose neighbor "just happened to have the same thing and what terrible things happened to her!" Very different illnesses may have similar sounding names. Vincent's angina is a severe throat infection, while cardiac angina is a sign of oxygen deprivation of the heart. The same illness can take different courses in different people depending upon specific and modifying circumstances. The diagnosis of serious illness is upsetting enough without being tortured by misinformation.

What Usually Happens in a Case Like This?

After you are comfortable that you understand what the doctor is saying, your job is not over. No diagnosis is written in stone.

Medicine is a series of careful approximations.
The complexity of the human organism,
both physical and emotional,
is far greater than human understanding.

With care, doctors try to reduce the margin of error to a very small measure, but it is never zero. One part of learning how to make a medical decision is understanding how secure the accuracy of the information is.

Technological complexity does not always lead to improved diagnosis. The more complicated the diagnostic technique, the more precisely formulated your question needs to be. Some patients who have had a diffuse fear of cancer have asked to have a "scan" of the whole body to make sure that they do not have any cancer. This is not a valid request. A CAT scan can show detail that cannot be seen by normal x-rays. It is possible to determine whether an abnormality is solid tissue or a fluid-filled cyst but a CAT scan cannot determine if the tissue is cancerous or benign.

Doctors may be able to make a good estimate as to the likelihood of there being cancer, but no one can know for sure without examining the tissue under a microscope. Some types of cancer may be hidden on a CAT scan because the difference in the x-ray characteristics between normal and malignant tissue is too small to permit detection. Some liver, ovarian and prostate tumors may fall into this category. Other kinds of tests would need to be done to secure a more detailed analysis of these. On the other hand, a CAT scan may show previously hidden birth abnormalities which look worrisome but are of no actual danger. One friend for whom a CAT scan of the brain was ordered for an episode of dizziness was making preparations for brain surgery until a more experienced reading of the x-ray confirmed that the abnormality was a simple cyst that had been present since birth.

If we ask the wrong question, the precision of technological wizardry may catapult doctor and patient even further from the right answer.

As you try to formulate the best approach to make a secure diagnosis, you have to have some idea of the expected natural course of the illness under consideration. Some illnesses may be so rapidly progressive and life threatening that the mere consideration of the diagnosis will obligate a physician to move quickly to treatment, sometimes with emergency surgery. A strong suspicion of appendicitis would not encourage a physician to delay surgery to do a CAT scan. Time can be critical and the proper decision may be to take the patient to the operating room after a urinalysis, chest x-ray and blood count. Even greater urgency would propel the surgeon if a ruptured Fallopian tube were suspected in early pregnancy. These are situations which can lead to precipitous death in otherwise healthy young people. Delay of diagnosis in such cases is far more dangerous than operating on a patient who may not have the feared condition.

On the other hand, an illness that could take ten years to produce complications should not be treated in a hasty fashion. High blood pressure can be deadly, producing strokes, heart attacks and kidney failure. Embarking on a lifetime of treatment may be an inappropriate response to a single high reading taken at a time when you were worried by some unusual stress. Knowing the natural history of the condition would allow a more measured approach to this finding of a temporary elevation of the blood pressure.

The natural course of an illness may not be the same for all populations. Prostate cancer in a man of fifty will usually have a very different course than prostate cancer in a man of eighty. The tumor tends to be much more aggressive and dangerous in the younger man. It will usually grow more quickly and spread more rapidly. However, this is not always true and occasionally you will find an older man with a very aggressive tumor. This only confirms the complexity of human life and disease and the inability to predict the future with the certainty that patients often expect or doctors would like.

Nevertheless, you will need some idea of the possible natural history of the illness and, once again, the first source of information should be the doctor who made the diagnosis. However, your doctor may not think to tell you unless you ask a question such as "What usually happens in a case like this?" The same medical encyclopedia that you consulted about diagnosis should provide some additional information about prognosis (another word for expected outcome).

What Can Be Done About It?

After gaining some idea of what the illness is and what the course of it may be, the next step is to consider what can be done about it. In most serious illness this usually means some medicine or surgery. The American idea of progress usually embraces a technological solution. The more spectacular the technology, the more it dazzles us, and the more we believe its power. Simple solutions seem weak; complicated solutions, powerful.

Most serious illness will require a complicated technological solution at some phase. We shall see later that some patients may reject the technological solution because of conflicts with other goals. Nevertheless the technological approach is often a valid alternative. However, there are still many illnesses which are best treated by a more technologically simple approach. The obese adult diabetic with a poorly healing infection of the big toe will be most benefited by a diet which will result in weight loss and blood sugar reduction. This may well result in a complete resolution of the problem. Similar benefits may accrue with abstinence from alcohol by a patient with alcoholic hepatitis or by a patient hemorrhaging from the enlarged veins of the esophagus found with alcoholic cirrhosis of the liver. The most current technology of the intensive care unit will be ultimately ineffective without the accomplishment of these low-tech solutions.

The Simple Case of Mr. Strong

Mr. Strong was injured in a head-on collision with another automobile on his way to work. In addition to the multiple bruises, he sustained a broken thigh bone. The paramedics came quickly in an ambulance. Their up-to-date, skilled training helped immobilize the injured limb as they transported him to the hospital emergency room. Once there, similarly well trained trauma physicians assessed the injuries, ascertained the otherwise good state of Mr. Strong's health and readied him for the operating room. The fracture was pinned and Mr. Strong was moved to the recovery room and then to his own room. He left the hospital ten days later to continue his physical therapy at home.

This is a simple and common story which lends itself clearly to analysis of the kind of medical decision-making we have been discussing. Its steps include information gathering, goal setting, treatment option selection, action and, if conditions change, goal evolution. Adhering to this sequence can clarify our thinking in more complicated circumstances.

Information-Gathering. The diagnosis was straightforward. Mr. Strong's thigh was swollen and painful when he was brought to the emergency room. An x-ray was taken which showed the fracture. There was little margin of error with respect to the diagnosis. The usual natural history of this condition may not be well known to most people, but without treatment the minimum assumption would be that the patient would be unable to walk properly. In fact, a fractured thigh bone is a serious, usually fatal injury in a society without sophisticated operative orthopedics. Hemorrhaging can occur in the thigh tissues that results in clots which can break off and travel to the lungs where they can cause death. If there is any break in the skin, infection can enter from the outside which rapidly spreads throughout the damaged tissues leading to abcesses and possibly gangrene. In addition, the fat of the bone marrow, which has been liberated from the shattered bone, can get into the bloodstream and travel to the lung and brain causing stroke and death.

Goal setting. Given Mr. Strong's previous good health and the absence of any associated disqualifying injuries which would have prevented full recovery, the obvious appropriate goal was the preservation of life and the restoration of function.

Treatment option selection. Technically, the choice of treatment options in Mr. Strong's case was simple. As long as the fracture was not so severe as to imperil the blood supply to the leg and make amputation a possibility, the patient did not have much interest in what particular hardware would be used to patch the bone together. Had the break been higher up in the hip, there might well have been some discussion of the types of hardware to be used, the anticipated length of time each type might be expected to provide good function and what kind of repair would be possible after that.

Action. The fracture was pinned.

Goal evolution. There might be complications in Mr. Strong's life on the basis of his injury. He could lose his job because of the length of time he would be out of work. He might become suicidally depressed because the bank foreclosed on his house when he was no longer able to pay his mortgage. Not really relevant to any particular medical decision that would have to have been made at any time after the accident, these are still consequences of the accident.

Although Mr. Strong had an uneventful recovery, this need not have been so. There are a small percentage of patients with his injury who will develop complications of either bone marrow fat clots or venous blood clots. Some patients will die abruptly when these occur. Others may suffer heart stoppages or low oxygen levels in the blood which can produce irreparable damage to the brain. Had this occurred to Mr. Strong, we would have been able to discuss the ways in which the original treatment goal may have evolved as the patient's condition deteriorated. We will have the opportunity to pursue this route in some of the stories to follow.

Different Versions of the Truth

Understanding alternative options of treatment will require more homework. The adage, "If you are a hammer, all the world's a nail . . ." is often true in medicine. When faced with a problem, the surgeon looks for a surgical solution, the internist a medicine solution, the radiotherapist a radiation solution, and the oncologist a chemotherapeutic solution. Each may honestly think his approach is best and each will, perhaps unconsciously, skew the evidence to support that contention.

Now you are faced with the problem of making a decision on the basis of different versions of the truth, each supported by a different expert. How do you solve this one when even the experts can't? This is where our medical decision-making structure is needed.

1. Find out if each expert agrees with the diagnosis. If they don't all agree, you can learn why they differ, which may relate to the different emphasis that is placed on each test.

2. If they agree on the diagnosis, do they agree as well on what may have caused this illness? Different treatment approaches may reflect different beliefs in causes.

3. If they agree on the diagnosis, is there general agreement on the natural history of the disease? Sometimes a difference in treatment approach will reflect a different set of values with respect to outcome. One expert may favor a radical approach because he feels obligated to prevent the infrequent but severe complication, while another will favor a lesser intervention which will be suitable for a majority of patients. This latter expert may feel that the more drastic approach should be saved for only those patients who demonstrate a failure of the less severe treatment.

This approach may coincide with or be the opposite of yours but you will never know unless you have some structured way of asking the consultants how they arrived at their opinions.

Our additional questions at this point would be, "What is your diagnosis? Is your diagnosis the same as that of Dr. X? If not, how is it different?" Try not to phrase questions in a way that would suggest you are pitting one doctor against another. You want the doctors to understand that you are just trying to gather adequate information to make an informed decision. You are not seeking fuel for a lawsuit. You are likely to get a much more informed discussion from the doctor if you admit what you don't understand. Your sounding too authoritative when you discuss topics about which you have just learned tends to cut short any discussion.

After discussing the diagnosis, take the opportunity to ask, "What may have caused this condition? Are there any other possibilities?" Don't be afraid to take notes. The doctor is going to use words that are familiar to him and probably not to you. His explanation will sound perfectly logical as he makes it, but you are likely to forget most of the argument by the time he turns the corner and heads down the corridor.

This is a good time to follow up with other questions about the illness. "What is the expected course of this condition? What would be likely to happen if no treatment were undertaken?" Here you will want to distinguish between possible outcomes and likely outcomes. Possible outcomes may include some terrible complications, while likely outcomes may be much less ominous.

Find out if all the consultants agree on the most likely outcome. If not, it's fair to say, "I don't understand. Dr. X said another outcome was more likely. Why would that be?"

This is an innocent way of approaching the professional differences of experts. You need the information. Don't be afraid to go after it.

Understanding Your Options

Only now, after you have understood the diagnosis, after you have been informed about theories of the cause of the disease, and after you have some idea about what may happen without treatment—only now are you ready for the meat of the matter, the treatment options.

Before you can begin to discuss actual choices, you have to understand the options. Before you can apply the standard of your goals to the choice of treatment, you have to appreciate both the dangers and the hoped-for results of each intervention.

What is the spectrum of possible results from each option? What is the most likely result of each option?

You will have to gather information about all the options, even the ones you may not be inclined to choose at first. As you become better informed about the possibilities, as you listen to each expert outline the benefits of that approach and the problems with the others, you will achieve a depth of knowledge that will provide you with a sound foundation for your decision. Again, you will rely on your family doctor for a coordinated view and you will want to consult your medical encyclopedia for another point of view, but you should try to talk to each of the consultants in person before embarking on an initial plan.

If this is sounding like a lot of work, that's because it is. If the illness is serious enough that you might die, either from the illness or its treatment, you had better become informed about your options. This is the point at which you will have the greatest opportunity to control the direction of your course. If you are too ill to do all this on your own, a designated family member or friend should be authorized to make some of these inquiries on your behalf. Nevertheless, the more you are able to participate, the more likely you will be to make the decision that is best for you. You will also find that you will become less afraid of the treatments you may have to endure. You will no longer see them as being done *to* you but rather *for* you. Furthermore, their nature and purpose will no longer be mysterious. The human imagination has the capacity to terrorize itself much more than the world actually can.

Familiarity will produce a serenity that will help strengthen you for whatever may lie ahead.

What are the general classes of treatment from which you will have to choose? The oldest are medicine and surgery. Before anesthesia, most decisions were almost always made in favor of medicine. After the invention of anesthesia, but before the advent of antibiotics, the frequent decision was in favor of surgery. Since the advent of antibiotics and other more powerful non-surgical treatments, there have been real choices among a plethora of alternatives for many illnesses.

Within surgery, there may be several alternative approaches. When I was first in practice, the standard operation done for a woman with breast cancer was a radical mastectomy, if she were "lucky" enough to have an early cancer with a favorable prognosis. A radical mastectomy was a very mutilating operation which not only removed the breast but also all of the accessible lymph nodes in the area as well as a layer of muscles down to the bones of the chest wall which were thereafter covered only by skin and the intercostal muscles found between the ribs. It usually required a skin graft to cover the operative area after the extensive surgery, and the woman would be left with a swollen arm for a long time, often forever.

This was a difficult operation to perform and a massive operation to endure. A great deal of prestige was attached to the surgeons who had developed the skill to perform it. No prestige was attached to the women who endured it. The mutilation made the bones of the chest wall stand out as in a skeleton and the beating of the heart could be seen quite easily beneath the thin layer of skin and intercostal muscle if it was the left breast which had been removed. In an era when the mysteries of the human body were still obscure to most Americans and the standard of physical beauty to which American women were expected to hold would not admit such a distortion, the psychological devastation of this operation was enormous. Many of the men who performed this operation were kind and deeply caring physicians who profoundly regretted what they felt obligated to do. It was only because they had seen other women die from unsuccessfully treated breast cancer that they could perform an operation which they believed was necessary to prevent that often painful death.

Over the years there were a substantial number of women who had what had appeared to be too large a tumor to be a good candidate for radical mastectomy. These women were treated in a variety of different ways. Some had only biopsies and then radiation. Some had local removal of tumor and radiation. Later, there were some who had various chemotherapy regimens after local tumor removal. What was surprising was how many of these women did better than was expected. They did not know that they were being given what the doctor thought was palliative (non-curative) treatment and many of them ended up cured!

With the better analysis of breast cancer statistics and the improvement of radiation and chemotherapy techniques, there are now few radical mastectomies performed and many lumpectomies (local removals) and simple mastectomies in which the muscles and many of the lymph nodes remain untouched. During the time of transition there were many surgeons who thought that performing less than a radical mastectomy was inadequate and would lead to women dying unnecessarily, while other surgeons performing the lesser surgery felt that the radical mastectomy was unnecessarily hard on the patient and useless. Before the statistics were conclusive there were many patients who agonized over the decision with their doctors. Both treatments were surgical approaches with the same ultimate objective of cure, but they were very different roads to that goal.

The contrast of the different degrees of surgery is echoed in the different approaches taken by medicine and surgery. The greatest contrast is highlighted in cardiac angina, the chest pain that occurs when the heart muscle is deprived of oxygen by a narrowing of an artery in the heart. Before the recent development of angioplasty, the stretching of the artery by a balloon passed into the blood vessel, the choices for the treatment of this condition were to bypass the narrowing by operating on the heart or to treat the condition by medicines which would reduce the oxygen needs of the muscle. This latter approach was augmented by diets which would, at the least, halt the progression of the narrowing and might hopefully actually result in the dissolving of the narrowing itself. The question was to determine which approach was the more successful.

Despite the expectation that surgery would have a greater impact on extending life, it turned out that the results were identical. This reflects, in part, the many different types of narrowing. Some narrowings are sparse and occur in large vessels that are easy to operate upon. Other narrowings are multiple and in small vessels that result in poorly functioning bypasses. The success of the medical approach also reflects the ability of the human body to heal itself. This occurs not just in the healing of skin wounds. The body itself is in a constant state of destruction and repair. If you can retard the destructive processes and augment the reparative processes, healing can often occur to a surprising degree.

Similar differences can be found in various approaches to

Grave's Disease (overactive thyroid) which can be treated by surgical removal of part of the gland, administration of medicine to block thyroid function, or the administration of a radioactive compound to destroy part of the gland.

How do you begin to make your choice among these alternatives? You have to learn what is entailed in each treatment. What is the best result for which you could hope from each course? But also, what kind of anesthesia and for how long? Where is the incision and how long will it take to heal? What are the possible and likely complications of this course? What kind of follow-up with what frequency of visits and what other tests will be part of the post-treatment course? What are the long-term consequences or side effects of each course? If the first course does not produce the desired result, can you try one of the others or does the selection of one forever prevent the subsequent choice of the others? These are the kinds of questions you must ask to gather the information you need to make a decision.

So far we have been discussing an illness in isolation. We have considered the name, the cause, the course and the treatment alternatives of the illness as if that illness existed disconnected from other factors—as if it had a reality and an existence apart from its reference to an actual person.

There is no illness other than as it occurs in individual patients. In each and every patient there are particular characteristics which alter both the presentation and the progression of the illness.

If there were no such variation, you would have a much easier time making a decision. After you have gathered all the information that you can about the illness that affects you, you then have to learn how that illness may be affected by the other features of your condition.

Lobar pneumococcal pneumonia is a common type of lung infection which, since the invention of penicillin, is usually treated very successfully. Nevertheless, there are many people who still die

25 QUESTIONS
YOU MAY WANT TO ASK YOUR DOCTOR

1. What is the name of this condition?
2. What does that mean is wrong?
3. What may have caused this?
4. Are there any other possibilities?
5. What can be done about it?
6. What usually happens in a case like this?
7. What's the expected course of this condition?
8. What are our options?
9. What would be likely to happen if no treatment were undertaken?
10. What's the spectrum of possible results from each option?
11. What's the best result for which you could hope from each option?
12. What kind of anesthesia and for how long?
13. Where is the incision and how long will it take to heal?
14. What are possible and likely complications of this course?
15. What kind of tests will be part of post-treatment?
16. With what frequency of visits?
17. What are the long-term consequences or side effects of each course of action?
18. If the first course doesn't produce desired results, can you try another? Does any course prevent subsequent choices?
19. When can I (or the patient) expect to feel better?
20. How does your diagnosis differ from that of Dr. X?
21. What other conditions do I have that can affect the course or treatment of my primary disease?
22. How much do you know about the interaction of these conditions with my primary illness?
23. How will these associated conditions alter the success of the several treatment options or the complications that I can expect?
24. Are these conditions permanent or temporary?
25. Is there anything we can do to eliminate these factors before you begin to treat my primary illness?

of this infection despite apparently adequate amounts of antibiotics. Why does this occur? What factors can modify this response? In some patients the pneumonia will come on top of some other medical catastrophe: a stroke, a heart attack with lung congestion or coma from a serious diabetic attack. In others, there may be a pre-existent lung condition which interferes with the patient's ability to respond to the antibiotics: emphysema, asthma or tuberculosis. In still others, there may be conditions which handicap the patient's immune system such as AIDS, leukemia or multiple myeloma, a disease that affects protective antibodies. Subsequent chapters will give us more of an understanding of the ways that people differ when exposed to a similar illness.

You need to know and to ask the questions that will help you ferret out the kind of information necessary to make good medical decisions. After you have the answers to these and similar questions, you can begin to apply the standards of your goals.

CHAPTER THREE

*Deciding on
Your Goals*

Learning to make a medical decision is pointless unless you have a goal in mind. All the questions and the search for information are useless unless you know the direction you want to travel. The medical data alone do not lead to a conclusion. The facts that you have acquired must be structured to support the pursuit of your goals. But those goals must be chosen before the medical data can have any relevance. How to choose those goals is the focus of our attention now.

Making Informed Decisions

If you ask most people why they go to the doctor, they will often reply, "To get better." Better than what? And what is "better"? Often this will be couched in terms of specific symptoms—the resolution of a cough or relief of back pain. Yet, a doctor doesn't usually think in terms of concrete pain alone. First there must be a diagnosis. This means the doctor has to offer an opinion as to what may be the *cause* of the problem. Without a general diagnosis, the choice of treatment is unlikely to provide lasting relief. The treatment of back pain due to cancer in the bone will respond to very different treatment than back pain due to muscle spasm from nervous tension, notwithstanding that the pain of the latter is sometimes more intense.

In the course of making a diagnosis, the doctor will usually want to first exclude the possibility that there is a serious or life-threatening cause for the symp-

tom. Many times this can be assured by the history alone and, in some
cases, this can be supported by the addition of a physical examination.

Many medical problems are self-limited.
This means you will get better with equal speed
whether you seek medical attention or pull the covers
over your head and wait for the symptoms to go away.

The doctor's job is to make a judgment about which symptoms are likely to be self-limited and which symptoms are more
likely to have a progressive course requiring more definitive treatment—which symptoms can lead to a proper diagnosis by themselves and which require more examination—whether physical,
blood tests, x-rays or even surgical exploration.

As the medical issue becomes progressively more complicated,
your goals begin to play a more important role.

The patient with a temporary back pain brought on by nervous tension seeks relief of the suffering. Usually this means the
administration of a pain reliever or a muscle relaxant or anti-inflammatory medication. Sometimes if the pain is aggravated by the
patient's fear that it is due to a cancer in the bone, a simple x-ray will
provide re-assurance and reduce the amount of medication
required. However, if the pain is due to an infection of the skin in
the back, a more definitive treatment with a surgical opening of the
infected area or the administration of an antibiotic will be required.
Here, the goal is no longer the relief of suffering alone but the cure
of a progressive condition before it gets worse.

A similar situation exists for the woman who presents her doctor with the new appearance of a small breast lump. Sometimes the
simple removal of the lump and some surrounding breast tissue will
be adequate to cure the disease. However, even this simplified situation is more complicated because the woman's psychological response
to the loss of some part of her breast needs to be considered.

**The concept of competing goals:
the desire for cure of a life-threatening cancer comes up against
a woman's desire to preserve the wholeness of her body.**

Most times this will be resolved in favor of the desire for cure and the woman will come to some psychological accommodation in the greater interest of remaining alive. But this is not the only possible choice and some women will choose types of treatment which will more completely preserve the appearance of the breast but be less sure as a method of conclusively eradicating the cancer.

This situation has its counterpart in men and the treatment of early localized cancer of the prostate. At the time that radical breast surgery was in fashion for women, the surgical treatment of prostate cancer was an extensive operation which left 20% of men unable to reliably hold their urine and 100% of men permanently impotent.

Increasingly sophisticated technology now allows us to make a diagnosis of prostate cancer many years before we would have been able to in the past. Now, surgical treatments are less extensive with greater success and the radiotherapy techniques are both more powerful and more precise. In the early signs of cancer, the traditional wisdom would indicate that the surgical approach still has a slightly better cure rate but a greater chance of impotence and other complications. If you are a man with this problem, you have to balance the importance of sexual performance with the greater chance of a longer life. It is a question of each man asserting his own goals on the basis of his own values.

A further complication can be seen in the case of a patient who develops leukemia or cancer of the blood-forming tissues of the bone marrow. There is no longer simply a localized disease to remove. Any treatment is going to have an influence on the whole body and all treatments will have significant side effects when they affect tissues other than the cancer cells. Some of these side effects will be uncomfortable, often very significantly so, others may be disfiguring as in the loss of hair and still others may be themselves seriously life-threatening by damaging the patient's immune system or predisposing to internal bleeding. At best, the treatment course will be difficult. If you are to have the resolve to withstand this technological assault you will have to be very sure that you have made an informed decision and thought carefully about your goals.

Four Primary Goals

There are four general goals you are likely to consider:
+ Cure
+ Extension of the length of life
+ Restoration of function
+ Relief of suffering

Which goal or factor you choose often depends on your assessment of the price you will have to pay. By price, I do not mean how much treatment will cost in dollars, although that will sometimes be a significant concern.

The price you pay is measured by pain, disfigurement, disability and alienation. These are not equal factors for each person or for each situation.

Each of these factors needs to be evaluated individually for each illness and, as we shall see later, that evaluation is likely to change as the course of the illness evolves. For now, you need to see what the dimensions of each of these factors may be.

The Many Faces of Pain

Try to think of a pain that caused you particular suffering—a broken ankle or your arm cut as you fell through a glass door. The pain did not begin instantly. There was a period of respite before the full enormity set in. Some part of this was the time required for the pain nerves to transmit the impulses through the circuits in your brain and some part of it was the time required for your brain to either amplify or dampen the intensity of those impulses by the psychological reaction to the event.

Pyschological effects. Fear may intensify the pain if you believe that worse things will happen because of the accident. Perhaps you were worried about tendons in your hand being cut, which could result in paralysis. Perhaps you were worried that the injury to your ankle would force you to miss the graduation prom. Both these concerns might make the pain worse. The opposite effect would result if you were intent on a goal which literally numbed you to pain. Your mind was so focused on that end that it would allow no other impulses to reach your consciousness. The pain endured in a fiercely contested football game or a gunshot wound suffered in rescuing a friend during a battle are typical examples.

Intensity. This is a pain factor which varies from one instance to another. Labor contractions and the pain of a kidney stone are more intense than the pain of a bee sting.

Duration. The labor contraction lets up after a while but the pain of a broken bone persists until it is relieved by medicine or stabilized by a cast. Knowing that the vomiting and headache of a cancer chemotherapy treatment will last for three days may well cause more suffering than the more intense pain of a kidney stone which you hope will pass quickly.

Every situation will mix these factors in a unique way which will have a very different meaning for each of us.

Confronting disfigurement. Disfigurement may be part of the disease or part of its treatment. The psychological cost of breast amputation, whether by radical or modified mastectomy, has already been mentioned. Similar issues may be important in the creation of artificial openings on the abdominal wall, such as colostomies or ileal bladders for the discharge of body wastes in patients for whom the rectum or the bladder have had to be removed to cure a cancer. The amputation of a limb for gangrene or the appearance of the characteristic purple skin lesions in Kaposi's Sarcoma in AIDS are additional examples. In some conditions, the disfigurement is part of the illness; in others it is the result of a choice that the patient makes in an attempt to overcome the illness. The psychological importance of such a bodily change can seriously interfere with your treatment choices if you don't confront this predicament honestly.

Disability considerations. This possible cost of illness and treatment may mean time away from work or from some other activity which is important to you. It may mean the inability to breath, run or see. Not all disabilities affect each of us in the same way. The loss of binocular vision which prevents you from playing tennis may not affect your ability to hit a golf ball. Duration of the disability also has both absolute and relative consequences. If recovery from surgery takes as long as your expected length of life, your enthusiasm for undergoing the treatment will be much less. If the recovery from surgery uses up a lot of "active life" time and leaves you with lower quality "passive life" time, why take the risk of surgery instead of just enjoying whatever time there is? How you analyze each prospective disability and its duration has a profound effect on your choice of treatment.

There are different meanings to alienation in medical treatment. To one patient it may mean a physician who fails to consider the human dimension of the therapy she recommends, the failure to see beyond the isolated technical description of the disease. To another, confined in the intensive care unit, sequestered from family and friends, alienation is the inability to get her emotional needs recognized in the face of institutional priorities. Yet another finds himself in an unfamiliar city undergoing fearsome treatments. The professional community can be very attentive but the patient may fear abandonment by those with whom he has had a short- term relationship. To each, the experience of previous professional relationships or the anticipation of how those relationships may evolve in the future can determine the selection of alternative therapies.

Likelihood of Benefit in Treatment

Not every treatment has an equal chance of success, nor is the likelihood of success necessarily higher with more difficult treatment. There are four basic variations in the benefit of treatment analysis:

✦ **Low price, great chance of benefit.** This category is exemplified by the administration of antibiotics for pneumonia. The likelihood of benefit is high, while the risk is small. Not every pneumonia will respond even if the bacteria tested appear to be susceptible to the particular antibiotic chosen. Some of the reasons for this have already been mentioned. Yet the risk is demonstrably small, although not zero. Some patients have allergic reactions to the antibiotic, which can range from a rash and fever to cardiovascular collapse and death. Major reactions occur very rarely, but their potential is always a concern when any medication is administered.

✦ **Low price, small chance of benefit.** It's like buying a lottery ticket. Your chance of winning is small, but if you win it could make a big difference. An example of this category would be the treatment of asthma by eliminating orange juice from the diet. Some patients with asthma are triggered by food sensitivities, some of which are triggered by ingestion of oranges. But to choose this as initial treatment is a long-shot, at best. Other examples of this group are "alternative" treatments used by patients with cancer or AIDS in addition to, or as a substitute for, conventional therapy when the side effects or complications of the usual approach become intolerable. The chance of benefit may be small but so are the side effects. Also, a sense of hope prevails.

✦ **High price, small chance of benefit.** This is a therapeutic approach which has little obvious appeal unless every other avenue has already been tried. Approaches with lower prices and greater likelihood of success will be tried first. But if there is still a chance of success in desperate illness, some people will want the opportunity, whatever the personal cost. This is the spirit behind those patients who offer themselves for experimental therapies. They may appreciate intellectually that the chance of success is small but a chance nevertheless remains. Emotionally each of these patients believes he or she could be the one whose program succeeds. An added reward is the knowledge that even if such a patient does not survive, the information gained may help fellow patients live in the future.

✦ **High price, high chance of benefit.** This treatment is characteristic of our modern, high technology approach to disease. The heart transplant, the chemotherapy of acute leukemia, the surgical reconstruction of the child with multiple birth deformities are concrete examples of the treatments in this group. It is with this group of treatments that there is the greatest difficulty in determining sound goals. These goals have to result from processing the facts of the illness through the web of the patient's values.

Personality Factors

Those who look ahead. Some people focus their energies on planning for the future. They live in anticipation of what is to be and tolerate the burdens of today as only a temporary annoyance. The response to serious illness becomes a measure of their basic attitude toward life. The most optimistic will concentrate on the ultimate resolution of the illness and will be undeterred by pain and/or personal costs.

Problems occur when there are unpredicted complications or interruptions in treatment. The problem is not the upset today but the implications this upset may have for the accuracy of the physician's other predictions. They threaten the security of long-term expectations and jeopardize the confidence of the patient in the soundness of the treatment decision.

Those who live in the moment. Other patients focus on the here and now. They have little concern about the future often because the problems of the moment loom large. One part of this may be personality trait, while another part could be the insistent demands of concrete circumstances. Short-term results and costs are more compelling than some vaguely hoped-for contingency of the future. How they are likely to choose among goals is different from their more future-focused counterparts.

Personality and the notion of courage are only two of the factors that can determine choice of goals. A sense of responsibility to others may influence goals in different ways. A young mother will have a different urgency to live for the protection of her children than an elderly man who has seen his family grow up and prosper. An eloquent affirmation of this motivation was provided by former Senator Paul

Tsongas who underwent a very difficult bone marrow transplant when his lymphoma relapsed after less drastic therapy. He remembered his own childhood, growing up without the mother who had died of tuberculosis. Despite the adversity he had already experienced and the uncertainty of the treatment's success, he took the opportunity almost eagerly because of his concern for his family.

Concern for family may result in very different choices among other patients. With older children who require more parental involvement in the present, a treatment that won't provide a long-term cure, but will let you be home to guide your children when they need it most, may have much more appeal. In a similar vein, a man who has been caring for his failing wife sick with the kidney failure of advanced diabetes may well choose a short-term radio-therapy program for his lung cancer than risk being away from her for as long as might be necessary for a more definitive cure.

Those who look at the past. As we shall see later, some goals will be modified by a patient's previous experience with technologically advanced but drastic treatments. Some have a very real limit to the intervention they will tolerate. Despite every likelihood of success, the curative treatment is rejected as if the pain and alienation of the prospective treatment were amplified by the previous experiences. The patient has become gun-shy rather than indifferent, just as some physicians, rather than becoming hardened by repeated experience, shrink from the imposition of more suffering on an already fragile patient. Essentially the personal cost to that patient becomes so high that the proposed treatment is rejected.

ANGELA JONES, AN INDOMITABLE SPIRIT

Angela Jones was an 80ish dowager whose daughter, granddaughters and son-in-law I took care of. It was only with the greatest reluctance that she came to see me. She had never had any major illness in her life and her previous doctor had died many years before. However, she was becoming progressively weaker and no matter how she changed her diet or tried a number of home tonics, nothing seemed to help. Although her history was not helpful in the diagnosis, by the time I was helping her to the examining room, my laboratory technician was knocking on the door to tell me that the blood tests indicated severe anemia.

As Mrs. Jones undressed, I hurried to the laboratory to review the blood slide. Indeed, there was a severe anemia and one that was characteristic of slow but profound blood loss. I returned to the examining room and carefully examined the patient but detected no characteristic findings. This by itself led to a presumptive diagnosis of a cancer of the right side of the colon. There were other possibilities but this was the most likely and the most serious.

When I told Mrs. Jones that the blood tests had indicated profound blood loss and that she needed urgent hospitalization to uncover the cause, she was adamantly against it. Finally, the increasing and unrelenting progress of her symptoms coupled with the pleadings of her daughter persuaded her to reconsider. Arrangements were made and a barium enema examination was scheduled for the next morning. When I came to see her after the barium x-ray to report the results, I found her recovered from her ordeal, dressed in a fresh dressing gown, pale but unbowed.

"Well, Mrs. Jones," I told her, "some part of the mystery has been solved. The x-ray today has shown us the cause of your weakness. There is a rather big tumor sitting in a silent part of your large bowel and it looks as if it has been bleeding slowly for a long time. I cannot be absolutely sure what kind of tumor this is but it is very clearly a kind that needs to be removed. It will have to be removed by surgery and I would advise you to have this done very soon."

"Doctor, that is not very good news at all," she replied. "I surely do not want to have an operation. I have lived over 80 years without an operation and I think it is too late to try this now. What kind of results would you expect operating on an old lady like me. Why ever would you imagine that I would survive? I think I'll just leave the hospital and go home and fade away gracefully, thank you."

"If you could be guaranteed of a graceful fading, I might agree with you," I told her. "And I can certainly understand your point of view. Unfortunately, given the location and size of your tumor, the far greater likelihood is that it will soon cause an obstruction to your intestines with pain, cramps and vomiting. Although we can relieve the pain, the vomiting and obstruction would require a tube in your nose and stomach to carry away the fluid. All of this does not constitute the peaceful ending you envision.

"If we operate soon, the likelihood is that the tumor will be completely removed and, after a period of recuperation you will be restored to your normal life. As you know, I am not a surgeon, but I will choose someone for you who has done this operation many times before and has had very good results. There is no guarantee of the results but everyone will try his hardest for you."

Mrs. Jones wanted to know how long the recuperation might be and how long she would have to be in the hospital. She asked whether she would need a colostomy and what complications we might expect. Her daughter was anxious that she have what she felt was a life-saving operation but she still questioned me carefully about the risks and recovery period. Finally, Mrs. Jones made a decision.

"I don't like it and I don't want it, but I don't have a choice. I certainly don't want to spend my last days vomiting all over my bed or let you put a tube in my nose. Call in your surgeon friend and let's get this over with as quickly as possible."

The operation was a success but the patient almost died. The strain of the fluid shifts on her old heart made her condition precarious for several days. Finally, she came around and her systems started working together again. Fortunately, she did not develop pneumonia or an abdominal infection. There was no blood clot or post-operative bleeding to complicate recovery. The naso-gastric tube stayed in only three days. The recuperation could begin. As soon as she felt strong enough, Mrs. Jones let me know how unhappy she was with the young resident doctor who came in every morning at 6 a.m. to draw her blood. "I don't know why he can't let me sleep. I'm too old to have some youngster stabbing me at that hour of the morning!"

Recuperation was slow as was expected with a woman of her years. She might be indomitably and mentally acute but her reserves for recovery were depleted by age. In making decisions about an operation, it is always important to weigh this factor carefully in the equation. Mrs. Jones spent three weeks in the hospital and then had to go live with her daughter for another month before it was safe for her to be alone for long periods. She was really not herself for over six months after the surgery. Nevertheless, after that time she was pretty much back to normal—and that was ten years ago!

There has been an appropriate diminution of energy with time but she travels across country with her family twice a year and plays an important and enjoyable role in her family's life. I generally get to see her only twice a year for checkups before her transcontinental trips.

Mrs. Jones' story is a good example of the process of medical decision- making.

Despite her advanced age and very attentive daughter, there was never any attempt to isolate her from the decision process.
She played an active role in choosing what would happen to her.

Her initial reluctance to accept my advice was dispelled when she learned the alternatives. Once she gathered information about the diagnosis, natural history and likely outcome, our paradigm was followed. She declared her own goals and, after a full discussion chose a course of action that would result in their accomplishment. While she was obviously unhappy with the pain and suffering she would have to endure, she felt sure that she was avoiding an even less desirable alternative.

Our Real Goals

As we mentioned earlier, if asked about the reason for a visit to the doctor, the patient will often answer, "To get better." If probed further, this will usually mean that the patient wants to be "cured" of some illness. This sounds normal and appropriate but it really represents an unexamined belief that whatever is troubling the patient can be magically made to go away as if nothing has happened. The laceration should heal without a scar. The pneumonia will heal without causing further loss of breathing function in the emphysematous lung. The damaged heart ought to heal without evidence of compromise in pumping ability during exercise. Obviously, none of these wishes is possible. Similarly impossible is the eradication of any cancer or high blood pressure or diabetes without some evidence of its previous presence or the necessity to continue medication.

There is no act of man or medicine
that will erase the evidence of life's struggle.
Serious illness will always have an enduring effect,
however wonderful the recovery.

There may be no perceptible loss of physical capacity, or the surgical scar may heal so that only the most intent search would discover it. Yet, the psychological footprints will be obvious to the knowledgeable. The experience may give the patient a feeling of strength that he has overcome such a fearsome obstacle. On the other hand it can sensitize the patient and make him unwilling to undergo such a trial again, whatever the expected outcome. Individual responses may vary throughout this spectrum of possibilities but each response is as valid as every other.

If our wish for cure is an unrealistic attempt to regenerate innocence, what is the best we can hope for? Earlier, we mentioned extension of life as a possible goal. This is a more concrete and attainable goal. However, except in some unusual circumstances it is not the mere prolongation of life that is our real goal. It is more likely that, as we think about it, we seek health and medical care as a means to attain the other goals in our lives. Some of these goals require intellectual acuity; others, physical dexterity. Whether it is the ability to see, hear, run, or an aspect of mental activity, some prolongation of life is usually necessary to make that ability meaningful.

The wish for a prolongation of life is really a part of the wish to have sufficient restoration of function to achieve the meaningful objectives of a patient's life.

Restoration of Function and Relief of Suffering. Every activity in medicine is likely to fall into either one or both of two fundamental, although sometimes competing, goal categories. If a particular treatment serves both purposes at a reasonable personal cost to the patient, there will be little doubt that this is an appropriate course of action. It may not be the only appropriate course of action, but at the very least there will be no argument about goals—only how to reach them most effectively.

Problems occur when goals are mutually exclusive and you must choose one or the other. Most American religious traditions are comfortable with a patient's capacity to choose between the relief of suffering and the prolongation of suffering even if lifespan is reduced by the choice. One of the exceptions is the Orthodox Jewish tradition which requires the patient and the physician to make preservation of life the highest priority since life, as the gift of God, may not be abridged by an act of man. On the other hand, no religion requires a patient to forego suffering if he chooses a more arduous route to maintaining the length of his life. The patient alone has the prerogative to make that choice.

Beyond the relief of suffering, medicine seeks to serve other patient needs. Extending life may be one of those but by choice of the patient, not the physician. Health is not an independent value. It is important to help a patient accomplish specific goals and to achieve a level of health which will permit the patient to accomplish those goals. If a patient seeks the extension of life to be able to finish a book, help a child complete his or her education or stand by a spouse's side as that spouse fights his or her own battles, these are understandable objectives to which anyone can subscribe. If a patient is willing to forego physical relief in order to extend life for these goals, no one would deny that opportunity. On the other hand, if a patient feels after sober consideration that the personal cost of extending life is greater than he or she can bear, it is inappropriate for that goal to be imposed on that patient.

As we shall see, there are times when the physician may abrogate that decision and substitute his judgment for the patient's choice. Often, he will do this believing in a "technological imperative"—the conviction that since a technological intervention is possible, it must be carried out.

If the primary role of the physician is relief of suffering, the "technological imperative" becomes irrelevant. Technology has no independent role except the benefit of the patient.

Using technology without the explicit permission of the patient is a perversion of the physician's role. A patient's option to take advantage of a new science, knowing the disadvantages as well as the advantages, is very different from having it imposed upon him. Establishment of goals is a patient's prerogative. Education and implementation are the physician's role.

There is an active movement in some areas of the United States to promote euthanasia—medically assisted suicide. I assure you that this is not what I am proposing. The patient must be able to count on the physician as his advocate at all times. If the patient and the physician confuse the physician's role, the patient's confidence may be shaken at just that time when he most needs support. While there may be instances in which a patient's suffering would be most effectively concluded by assisting him to die, the relief the patient usually seeks is not death, but a more tolerable life.

How to best assist the patient in achieving this goal is not easy and represents the art of a family doctor. It may be technically more difficult to relieve a patient's pain, but the emotional reward is so much greater. However, if treatment hastens a patient's death while relieving pain, there is no conflict. The primary aim was the relief of suffering—not the death of the patient.

All of these considerations are a lot of work and usually come at a time when you may be feeling pretty depleted, both physically and emotionally. I recommended earlier that you try to choose a particular family member or close friend who can help you keep track of this process. The person you choose should be a good listener as well as a good questioner.

Sometimes you will not really know what is the most important goal until you have had a chance to talk about it.

We have considered some very complicated topics. We have looked at ways of determining the facts of illness and have tried to understand the implications of those facts with respect to specific treatments. We have thought about the issues involved in making a medical decision and analyzed many of the factors to be considered when establishing goals in serious illness—not only the choices but the cost attendant to each choice. We have mentioned competing goals, likelihood of benefit from treatment, and personality factors in decisions.

Here are a few points you may want to remember:

It is necessary to define your goals, based on four primary goals:

✦ Cure
✦ Extension of the length of life
✦ Restoration of function
✦ Relief of suffering

Each goal must be evaluated individually for any illness. Evaluation changes as the course of an illness evolves.

Pain has many faces:

✦ Psychological effects
✦ Intensity
✦ Duration
✦ Disfigurement
✦ Disability

The psychological and physical importance of all of these can affect your treatment choices.

Likelihood of benefit in treatment:

✦ Low price, great chance of benefit
✦ Low price, small chance of benefit
✦ High price, small chance of benefit
✦ High price, great chance of benefit

These goals must result from processing the facts of the illness through the web of the patient's values.

Medical technology has no independent role besides the benefit of the patient.

CHAPTER FOUR

Allowing Your Goals to Evolve

Modern hospitals are awesome places. They abound with science fiction feats, such as heart transplantation and hypothermic suspension of life to allow impossible brain operations. These hospitals that make such feats commonplace are the culmination of 400 years of scientific thought that began in the Renaissance. The essential novelty at that time was the focus on measurable features of the physical universe. The world of divine forces and magical influences, sorcerers and wizards gave way to measurement of the movement of the stars and planets in the heavens and the measurement of falling spheres on Earth.

In the study of mankind, the philosopher Descartes separated mind and body. The emphasis since then has been clearly on the body. Today, however, when choosing goals of medical treatment, we must re-allow some Renaissance thinking. We must not emphasize physical objectives so much that we ignore emotional and spiritual values, which we have learned are so important to success.

In the last chapter, our discussion of essential medical goals boiled down to the restoration of function and the relief of suffering. The goals of cure and extension of life are really subsets of these objectives. Suffering clearly has a psychic dimension which we can all recognize, but no less so does the restoration of function. Function is not just being able to raise an arthritic shoulder to a particular angle. Function is really assessed in terms of *what specifically* you can do.

If the doctor tells you you will be able elevate your shoulder to thirty degrees, that is not nearly so important as knowing that you can comb your hair or put on your earrings or wash behind your ears.

Similarly, measurements of other motions may mean that you will be able to clean yourself at the toilet rather than depending on someone else. The independence and esthetic improvements of those accomplishments cannot be measured by a recitation of angles and weights alone.

Goals Can Change

Until now we have been referring to medical decisions and goals as if you had only to make a choice once in the course of the illness and everything would evolve from that. For better or for worse this is not so. No situation is static. Each point is like a single frame out of a movie. Life is dynamic, and no serious illness is so predictable that it will behave entirely to form. Goals change. Different values become important. No person has such narrow objectives that as the situation changes there will be no change in the goal toward which treatment is directed. As any illness evolves—as complications develop or therapy is more effective than anticipated—there should be a frequent reassessment of treatment goals. Sometimes the circumstances will change quickly in a rapidly progressing illness. At other times they will evolve more slowly over years. You need to review whether the facts and hopes that governed your initial decisions still hold.

One of the great mistakes that patients and physicians often make is believing that once they have embarked on a certain course, the direction of that course is unchangeable.

The exact opposite is the case and we all depend on this flexibility to give us the courage to attempt the difficult. Knowing that if the first approach has unsought consequences the plan can be modified allows us to embark upon the bold course. Under most circumstances the initial attack on a new illness in an otherwise healthy person will be vigorous. Not many people will want to give themselves up to illness without some struggle. How far each may be willing to carry that struggle is an individual decision requiring analysis of the issues we have been discussing.

There are only a few instances in which a decision to change course will not allow us to salvage something from a bold attack thwarted by circumstance. While it is true that you cannot un-perform an operation, there are actually times when the doctor can begin an operation and change goals in the middle of it. This change of goals will not be done with the patient's consultation at that moment but as a result of the patient's situation, calling for the priority of different alternatives in the preoperative visits with the surgeon. However much we may prepare and attempt to gather all the relevant information before undertaking a potentially perilous intervention, there will always be surprises. Uncertainty is ever the companion of great undertakings.

Quality of Life vs. Duration of Life

There are two common ways in which goals can change as illness evolves. You may choose to accept a lower level of functioning than you might have before or you may accede to a shorter duration of life in order to preserve life's quality. Rarely do we have the opportunity to consider new options because of unexpected success of a treatment program. The acceptance of a lower level of functioning is what happened with my mother, as related in Chapter One. The step-like decline was made tolerable psychologically because the plateau of that step was at least higher than the more severe descent of the original collapse. Mother had a real sense of improvement from either the pain or the breathlessness so that whatever limitations remained were less than what had been. Similar progress can be seen in the treatment of acute infection in emphysema or paralysis in strokes.

The decision to choose a shorter duration of life is rarely made as a positive goal. Our goal becomes the tenacious preservation of what quality of life we may have which usually leads to a diminished emphasis on the length of that life. The maintenance of today's breathing capacity, today's mobility or today's comfort becomes a more important goal than risking what you have in an attempt to treat some underlying and progressive condition. The future becomes less important than the present. The evolution of our goals is generally what underscores that shift of our concern to the present.

As our focus changes from the original goal of cure to the relief of suffering, the patient and his family will often see this as defeat. In one way, it clearly is. Yet the old adage about not crying over spilled milk has an important message. None of us ever asks for illness. Illness comes as an unwelcome visitor. Even if we are able to make this visitor disappear, the footprints remain. Our best result and our most satisfactory strategy will require us to be candid about the situation as it is. Wishful thinking and magical beliefs will lead only to wrong solutions.

The topic of magical thinking is a key to the issues of medical decision-making and goal-choosing. Distinguishing between hope and wish is the separation of reality from illusion. Hope is based on real possibilities, however unlikely. Wish is for possibilities that can't exist in the world as we know it. The dizzying advances of technology have often blurred the line between hope and wish and provided an apparent foundation for wish because almost anything seems possible.

Doctors are no less susceptible to the appeal of wishing than are patients. The patient wishing for the impossible cure is matched by the doctor wishing for the chance to perform that impossible cure. Both seek to avoid unpleasant reality by a flight to fantasy, conspiring to pretend that they can repeal the laws of nature. The doctor praises the patient's courage. The patient returns the compliment by celebrating the doctor's special knowledge and talents which will allow that doctor to succeed where others would fail. This mutual seduction will usually end in disillusionment and recriminations, if not a malpractice suit. Each participant will blame the other for not fulfilling the unrealistic expectations.

Inventing imaginary circumstances cannot help us make choices more successfully. Rather than recasting the world in a form that will allow us to pretend that we can make wish reality, both doctor and patient have to explore the real limits of possibility. It is much harder to work out these possibilities than to indulge in the romantic fiction of our wishes. The doctor must learn not to require the patient to exhibit an unthinking bravado nor to allow the patient to force the physician to assume a heroic mantle.

We have to make choices based on an accurate understanding of our alternatives. That understanding demands an entirely truthful characterization of our situation.

We must make the best choice from the possibilities we have. We cannot wish that the possibilities were different and feel defeated because the choices that are allowed us are not as full as the ones we would hope for. The measure of our success is how closely our choices come to the best possible outcome.

We are successful if, working together, we have made the best use of our possibilities.

An example is the family into which is born a child with Down's Syndrome. This is a congenital condition resulting from an error in chromosomal number which produces moderately severe mental retardation. It affects the genetic material of every cell in the body and is not amenable to cure. Any family who rushes around searching for a cure is dissipating energies that are urgently needed in other areas of care for this child.

It is understandable that the family feels devastated and they are deserving of our human empathy, but nothing we know will cure the child. This, however, is not to say that there is nothing to be done. There is a lot to be done in helping the child explore his potential. Not every child with Down's Syndrome will have the same abilities. Discovering what your child may be able to accomplish and devising ways to help him on that journey are important family functions. Magical thinking in the search for a cure will distract all concerned from the difficult but productive efforts to be expended in helping this child find a place in the world.

As illness winds down to the finish line, we focus more intently on the problems of the moment and how effectively we can relieve them. The longer term issues recede as the ultimate outcome is accepted with resignation. If death is defeat then we will all die defeated but, in any case, die we all will. As we explore the experiences of others, it will become clear that the end is not the same for everyone. There are many things we can do to make it better. Along the way, there are victories of the spirit as well as the flesh. Both pride and pleasure can accompany the struggle.

The body is in a constant dynamic of dissolution and repair. Some mechanisms transport cholesterol into the blood vessel wall and others move it out. The forces of bone erosion are countered by those of new bone formation. Even if the dissolution phase is dominant, there is always some evidence of repair from which we can gain hope. The sudden loss of function from a stroke is almost always followed by the return of some function as the body adapts to the catastrophe. Until the next blow, our focus is on that improvement from the nadir. If we are intent on the immediate problems—nausea, pain, shortness of breath—we can solve each one at least temporarily to some extent. If the cost to the patient in terms of grogginess may be unacceptable at times, that is only because there is some other goal which has a higher priority. The accomplishment of that goal, whatever it may be, then provides a focus for the patient's thoughts and serves as a support in this decline.

To focus on the concrete problems of illness provides an important diversion for a patient with serious illness, giving the patient some sense of control.

The human imagination is a most potent instrument of terror. The human mind has a capacity to imagine horrors which are much beyond the power of the cosmos to produce. If you allow yourself to focus on the uncertainties ahead, the mysterious unknown, your energies become dissipated in this formless torment of the mind. No situation is as terrible in the concrete as we can create in our imaginations. The terror with which we color our fears is evidence of the same imagination which can help us find victory in apparent defeat.

The sense of hopelessness that may overtake us as we consider the natural progress of disease should be separated from our human concern for the patient. The doctor may have no further intervention that will produce any benefit in holding off the disease. Every avenue may have already been explored. Yet the patient is different from the disease and there is never a time when there is nothing further that can be done. The relief of suffering, whether the administration of morphine for pain or the gentle words of the caring friend to stave off the fear of abandonment in the time of distress, addresses those human needs. They may not change the course of the disease but they both relieve the human suffering that accompanies it.

BETSY & SHEILA WATKINS

Betsy Watkins felt weak on her way back from the mailbox. She was alone in the house. Her daughter had left for work an hour ago and Betsy hadn't told her about the dizzy spells that she had been getting over the last month. She was afraid that it would mean another trip to the hospital and she knew she could not handle another round of that.

It had all started five years ago when she went to Dr. Smyth for a touch of bronchitis and he had insisted on examining her more completely and found that lump in her breast. She knew it was there but it hadn't bothered her and she did not see why she had to go through all those tests. In the end they had removed the lump which was malignant and had said that there was some evidence that it may have spread since a couple of lymph nodes were involved. The doctor and her daughter had insisted that she take the chemotherapy treatments, which were really horrible.

She finally got up the courage to tell them she would not take the treatments any longer; she did not care what the consequences were. At her age, living with those treatments was much worse than dying without them. Her daughter pleaded with her but she was adamant. In the end they all agreed that she would take a couple of pills which had showed promise in holding off the tumor but were not so strong that they would cure the tumor or kill her.

A delivery man saw Mrs. Watkins slumped on the sidewalk and ran to his truck to have his dispatcher call for an ambulance. It came quickly and swiftly and carried the unconscious lady to the hospital emergency room. There intravenous lines were begun, an electrocardiographic monitor was attached and an endotracheal tube was placed in the still unconscious woman's throat. She would never talk again. When doctors would remove the tube, she would be dead.

By the time Sheila was summoned from work her mother was already in the intensive care unit. The last time her mother was in the hospital she had made Sheila promise that whatever happened, Sheila would not force her to go back in the hospital and never in that intensive care unit. If she had to die, she wanted it to be peaceful and quiet, not with all those strangers and noises and lights that made it seem you were already in Purgatory, being tortured.

Sheila had made the promise because her mother asked for it and she could not refuse. But she did not want to do it. Her mother was the only one left and she could not think of life without her. As long as there was life in her mother, Sheila would do anything to preserve it, despite her mother's wishes. Now all the agony of decision-making had been taken away. The doctors were in charge and they were going to do everything to bring her mother back again, even if her mother did not want it.

Mrs. Watkins' doctor was away at a medical meeting and the doctor who was covering did not know her since Mrs. Watkins had avoided seeing any doctors after her chemotherapy experience. Dr. More, the covering doctor, spoke to Sheila in the hall outside the intensive care unit. It looked very bad indeed. The tumor had spread to the brain where it had remained in a hidden area until this morning when, the tests showed, a blood vessel in the midst of it had leaked and resulted in a substantial hemorrhage. The hemorrhage stopped now but there was too much damage to inspire hope that her mother would recover. She probably would not even be able to maintain breathing if the endotracheal tube in her throat were removed.

Dr. More asked Sheila whether her mother had signed a "living will" or had in any way made known her wishes about proceeding in circumstances such as these. Sheila said that her mother had not made a living will, and indeed she had not. Mrs. Watkins was so anxious to stay away from doctors that she was not even aware that a piece of paper detailing her wishes could have helped protect her from the treatments she feared so much. Sheila was still in shock from the recognition that her mother was so gravely ill. She could not bear to reveal that her mother had stated many times that she "did not want to be kept alive by any of those machines in the hospital and that she wanted to die like a human being." If Sheila told the doctors this, they would slacken their efforts, her mother would die sooner and she would be left alone.

Sheila prayed for a miracle every day, several times a day, week after week. Mrs. Watkins suffered many life-threatening complications: blood poisoning from bacteria in the urinary tract one week, pneumonia the next week and a bleeding ulcer after that. Each time Dr. More asked Sheila what she thought her mother would want done. Did she want more aggressive antibiotics even though they might lead to other complications and would not restore her health and mind but only perpetuate this vegetative state? Did she want the additional tubes and irrigations of her stomach to treat the stomach hemorrhage? Or would her mother have wanted to be kept comfortable as the inevitable conclusion of life came peacefully?

Each time Sheila said to go on. She said her mother would have wanted everything done that could be done. Sheila knew she was lying but she could never live with herself if she thought that she had given an order that would result in her mother's death. She believed that she would always think of herself as her mother's murderer. When she prayed for miracles now, she began to pray that the doctor would stop asking her these questions because she couldn't handle them any longer.

She knew her mother would have wanted to stop all of this, and yet she couldn't bear the thought of being the one to stop it.

She wanted her mother to live and she didn't want her mother to live. Not this way, not the way her mother always dreaded.

Sheila worried about her mother's soul. Was it still imprisoned in that tortured and unresponsive body or had it already left and was in a more contented place even now? The platitudes of her clergyman did not help because this was her mother—not some abstraction. Sheila thought she was losing her mind because on the one hand she wanted her mother to live and on the other she wanted her mother to be relieved of this pain. These were obviously contradictory thoughts and only crazy people could think opposite ideas at the same time. She must be crazy.

Finally in the eighth week of the vigil, Mrs. Watkins developed a fungal pneumonia that did not respond to any of the most sophisticated treatments and she died with a team of five specialists and nurses pounding on her and trying to force oxygen into the unyielding lungs. Her trial was over but Sheila's trial continued because she was now consumed by guilt that she had not honored her mother's wishes, that she had been selfish in refusing to allow the doctors to suspend aggressive treatment, and furthermore that she had lied to accomplish this.

Sheila was overwhelmed by it all. The grief she couldn't express distorted her judgment. The choices she had been asked to choose from were, every one of them, horrible. The ambivalence about wanting her mother to live or be released from pain confused her. She knew that she was not thinking clearly. In addition to her grief and guilt, she suffered the worry that she was going crazy. The physiological problems of Mrs. Watkins's illness were complicated but not nearly so trying as the terrible emotional turmoil that she and her daughter experienced.

Dealing With Issues in Advance

If Mrs. Watkins had been treated respectfully as the competent judge of her life and values, this story would have been very different. There was no consideration of her wishes because, in the guise of protecting her from bad news, she was not given information about her illness, its nature and expected course to which she was surely entitled. She was told that she had a condition that could respond to treatment and not to worry. Mrs. Watkins was no college graduate but neither was she a fool. Doctors did not remove a woman's breast to treat constipation. Obviously she must have cancer, and even if she would not say the word out loud, it must be pretty hopeless or else Sheila would have talked about how she was cured instead of talking all that mumbo-jumbo with the doctor.

Mrs. Watkins tried hard to get Sheila and the doctor to accept her goals. However, since they had not involved her in the discussion of the disease itself and its prognosis, they could not very well talk to her about goals without spilling the beans they had tried so hard to hide. Besides erroneously thinking that she was protecting her mother from worry by not talking to her about her cancer, Sheila had another reason for avoiding a discussion. She was pretty sure that her mother had a very different set of goals and that life at any cost was not among them. By avoiding any medical discussions, Sheila could make all the decisions.

Mrs. Watkins' treatment in the Emergency room was swift and appropriate. The emergency room staff had no way of knowing her history and their presumption had to be that she wished vigorous treatment. However, her struggles in the intensive care unit were a very different story. If her true wishes about heroic measures had been known, she would not have been required to suffer each of the succeeding groups of treatment. Mrs. Watkins' life could very well have been allowed to wind down when it was clear that no restoration of function was possible. The change in goals as complications developed or new information became available would have allowed a relatively easy transition. The vigorous approach of the emergency room could have been curbed and the natural course of the brain hemorrhage permitted to evolve.

Our analysis of the issues of medical decision-making and the application of the results are valid even if the participants failed to make use of them. Angela Jones' story from the last chapter had a happy ending. She recovered completely and continued to live a productive and meaningful life with her family. How would everyone have felt if she had died of a heart attack following surgery or suffered a stroke which would prevent her from being able to continue living alone? Mrs. Jones recognized death as one possible outcome of her medical adventure, and that did not frighten her. A disabling stroke would have been a different issue altogether. If the stroke were sufficiently severe, her "living will" would have prohibited us from subjecting her to the heroic treatments that would prolong her dying. If the stroke were less severe, my guess is that she would have been quite vexed but would have learned to adjust.

In any case this illustrates the necessity and importance of changing goals as the situation changes. The fact that our initial approach to a problem is vigorous does not mean that we are committed to life at any cost if serious complications develop. Mrs. Jones charged us with the responsibility of understanding her wishes and changing the goals as might be required to fulfill those wishes.

These true stories begin to isolate the problems we have in trying to think about people and illness. Many situations like those of Mr. Strong, referred to in Chapter Two, are easy. It is seductive to think that all situations have as obvious an approach. The power and ingenuity of our science may lead us to believe that if only we try hard enough, all medical problems can be solved this successfully. This is the fallacy that has caused so much pain to patients and anguish to so many families. There is still lots to do medically and life to live but the emphasis, time scale and goals must be different.

**There is a point beyond which repair is not possible.,
when goals must change; the pursuit of cure falls away
and concern with comfort, communication and love become
very much more important.**

Mrs. Jones' story illustrates that merely because someone is old is no indication to forego the possibility of radical aggressive cure. If a disease is at a stage and the patient is in a condition in which cure is a reasonable possibility, let's do it. An isolated breast cancer would be a typical example. The nature of the surgical treatment is usually easily tolerated and the failure to treat will have terrible consequences. This is true whether the patient is 35 or 85.

A difficult decision may arise with respect to follow-up treatment—whether the patient may require radiotherapy, chemotherapy or no treatment. Very different decisions may be made depending upon the patient's wishes, goals and physical abilities.

The Fear of Indignity and Pain

Mrs. Jones' story was really much more complicated than this. There was a real possibility that she might not survive the surgery, and she was willing to take that chance. Most old people do not fear death. They are more likely to fear the indignity and pain on the way. Mrs. Jones clearly preferred to die during surgery than to die in the way that might be anticipated without surgery—invaded by tubes, overcome by vomiting and pain. There was still a reasonable expectation that she could be cured and with cure would experience a significant and valuable extension of her life. Furthermore, that life would be lived in what, to her, was a normal way. For example, we did not have to debate her ability to deal with a colostomy, an opening created on the belly wall for the excretion of feces when the tumor is so low in the intestine that the rectum must be removed.

Other problems arise when the nature of a surgery, even if curative, creates a situation which may be seriously disabling or debilitating in itself. Examples would include major amputation of a leg in a diabetic with gangrene, or the removal of a kidney in a patient who would then have to become a chronic dialysis patient for the rest of his life. These are situations in which patients might differ on their enthusiasm or acceptance of curative surgery depending on other physical and emotional circumstances.

Each of these situations is unique and the values that each patient and family brings to them is unique. There is no single answer or approach that is appropriate to all.

Mrs. Jones had signed a "living will" before surgery. In it she had made quite explicit her wishes about life-support systems—

breathing machines, dialysis treatments and feeding systems which might be used to support someone's life while repair or treatment of some organ system might proceed. She was quite clear that we were forbidden to institute these measures unless it was for a limited period of time with the expectation that she would recover with the ability to live an independent life.

When Mrs. Jones signed this document it did not have the force of law in New York but was nevertheless a clear expression of her considered wishes and one which her family and I took as a moral imperative. In the intervening years, the New York State legislature has written an excellent law which does allow patient expression with the legal expectation that the patient's wishes will be followed.

Another decision may be to appoint a "health care proxy," that is, someone who will have the right and responsibility to make decisions on the patient's behalf if he should be unable to act because of accident or the progression of disease. A more complete discussion of these provisions will be found in a later chapter.

Mrs. Watkins' tragic story reflects all the consequences of not dealing with these issues in advance. She had been intimidated into accepting a debilitating chemotherapy course without having a clear idea of the goals and consequences. When she finally called a halt she opted out of any relationship with a doctor. There was no authority to whom she could express her wishes and fears so that a collaboration would result. She did not have a written expression of her wishes to act as a guide for others when she became incapacitated. She did not have the opportunity to discuss her wishes with her daughter in a way that would elicit her daughter's cooperation and ease the burden of guilt that her daughter might feel in carrying out her mother's wishes.

Even with a living will and the cooperation of her daughter, Mrs. Watkins would probably have been intubated by the ambulance emergency personnel or by the emergency room physicians when her breathing became inadequate. Most people with living wills do not wear a copy around their necks, and emergency personnel should not waste time debating moral imperatives when responding to a crisis. Although the use of the breathing tube clearly extended the length of Mrs. Watkins' life under circumstances she did not want, the knowledge of her wishes during that first day would have prevented the addition of medicines and other treatments which made her ultimate death so prolonged.

Age should not be an impediment to cure and neither should it cause hesitation among emergency personnel in administering potentially life-saving and preserving treatment immediately to people who might benefit.

It is in the escalation of medical intervention, in inappropriate circumstances, that medical treatment becomes medical torture.

Sheila Watkins suffered terribly during her mother's illness. Her mother was a quiet and private person who did not share her feelings about events and goals easily or in an articulate way. Nevertheless in her devotion to her daughter's education and to maintaining a stable supportive home, she demonstrated by example the strength which Sheila took as the basis for her own very considerable success in the business world.

Sheila took a positive view of the world and her ability to solve problems. She enjoyed reading about the progress of medicine and the astonishing reports of organ transplants and biologic mysteries unmasked.

Stories and television news reports rarely give any sense of the difficulty to the patient in maintaining these "miracles."

The operation is performed successfully and the patient lives happily ever after. The hourly monitoring of blood pressure, blood sugar or urine flow is ignored. The every four-hour administration of pills, the daily taking of blood to assess the stability of the intervention is glossed over. The rushed trips back to the hospital when the medication levels get either too high or too low go unreported. When Mrs. Watkins suffered awful complications of the chemotherapy after her operation, Sheila was both surprised and disappointed. All the stories she had read reported patients heroically overcoming these problems. She interpreted her mother's reactions as evidence of weakness of will and commitment. Sheila was surprised by this weakness in someone to whom she had always looked as the source of her own strength, and she was disappointed that her mother would fail her in a job so important as the preservation of her own life.

Sheila was ignorant of the variability of response to medication in general and chemotherapy in particular. One dose of cyclophosphamide might have no observable effect, good or bad, on one person and still wipe out the bone marrow of another. The weakness and nausea that Mrs. Watkins suffered created a gulf between Sheila and her mother that exacerbated the worry and tension that Sheila felt from simply having her mother sick at all.

Mrs. Watkins had withdrawn more. She could not understand how her daughter could be so cruel. The medicine was making her feel so bad and her daughter didn't seem to care. When Sheila was sick as a child she had certainly nursed her with much more love and concern. All Sheila did was shout that she had to take the medicine; and when they went to the doctor together, Sheila and the doctor spoke mumbo-jumbo together as if she weren't there at all. In so doing, Sheila could be sure that her mother would not interfere with Sheila's wish that she have the benefit of all treatment that might extend her life. Unfortunately, this well meaning but condescending attitude had the opposite effect. Instead of being allowed to participate as a collaborator, Mrs. Watkins was made to feel like a victim. Instead of feeling that these harsh treatments were being done *for* her, she felt they were being done *to* her, and she refused to have any part of them. Her final, almost self-destructive, act of defiance was flushing the mild chemotherapy pills down the toilet as a daily affirmation that she would choose her own course.

Sheila's suffering became more serious than just disappointment at her mother's imagined moral weakness. She was tortured by the dilemma of honoring her mother's stated wishes about "life support" versus her fear of forever thinking of herself as a participant in murder for telling the doctors about her mother's instructions.

Since Sheila had not really spoken to her mother in any way to explore her feelings, she didn't know the depth and coherence of her mother's views. At that time she was just concerned about her own feelings of potential loss and thought that she was honoring her mother more by refusing to consider that she would one day be gone.

As the vigil continued, Sheila developed further concern about her own sanity. She was tortured by the alternation of her feelings that she must prolong her mother's life at any cost with the recognition that her mother was surely going to die soon and had earned a peaceful conclusion to her hard-fought life. The success of Sheila's life had depended on her ability to choose a course of action and stick to it undeterred by obstacles. She had never been intimidated by long hours or long odds; nor had she ever shirked a difficult decision. She had always been able to weigh alternatives and be satisfied with her conclusion. This business with her mother produced confusion and tension. She couldn't settle on a single thought. This capacity to hold contradictory thoughts at the same time is called ambivalence, and we will spend more time exploring it in a subsequent chapter.

The vignettes we've just discussed exemplify the importance of two crucial issues in dealing with illness:

1. **Medical decision-making includes information gathering, goal setting, consideration of treatment options and acknowledgement that goals change as illness evolves.** In undertaking information gathering, we learn the diagnosis, assess the possibility of error, understand the causes of illness, the natural history of untreated illness, and what would be a likely outcome in the specific circumstances.

2. Planning for the future and communicating a patient's wishes to the family helps the process of goal-setting.
Important to dealing with specific illness, goal-setting is important in planning for the future generally. Serious illness does not always give you enough warning to take care of problems when they arise. The best time to think about goals is free from the pressure of specific illness. Every person concerned should have an opportunity to express wishes, when an attempt to reconcile conflicting views can be made without the sense of urgency that a deteriorating medical condition may induce.

A later chapter will review in more detail the features of living wills and healthcare proxies which can assure patients that their wishes will be followed. Sheila Watkins was as much a tragic victim of her mother's last illness as was Mrs. Watkins. Her intentions were honorable if misguided.

The path that Sheila and her mother's doctor took at the beginning of the illness determined the problems that would interfere with communication as the illness progressed.

You rarely have the opportunity to rebuild credibility once you have lost it. Sheila lost the chance to spend her mother's last years, months or weeks in the loving companionship that would have meant so much to them both. Rather than having happy memories of times spent together, Sheila will be tortured for a long time to come by doubts about how she acted and even by her own sanity.

The stress and pain of severe family illness takes its toll on everyone. Yet, communication and a common plan can ease that pain and provide both patient and family with a sense of accomplishment and inner peace, whatever the outcome.

In allowing your goals to evolve it's important to remember that:

✦ The decision to choose a shorter duration of life is rarely seen as a positive goal, but it can be. As focus changes from the original goal of cure to the relief of suffering, our perspective can change.

✦ Distinguishing between hope and wish is the separation of reality from illusion.

✦ Choices need to be based on an accurate understanding of our alternatives. Understanding demands an entirely truthful characterization of the situation.

✦ The patient is different from the disease, and there is never a time when there is nothing further than can be done.

✦ Each situation is unique, and the values that each patient and family brings to them is unique. There is no single answer or approach that is appropriate to all.

✦ Communication and a common plan can ease pain and provide both patient and family with a sense of accomplishment and inner peace.

CHAPTER FIVE

What to Do When Things Change

Real patient stories show how the way we analyze a medical crisis can help us reach our goals with greater certainty. These stories also demonstrate that to achieve our goal, each situation may require emphasis on a different factor. In some cases, information gathering is the most important feature. You have to learn what you may be up against, particularly the natural course of illness and its most likely outcome. In other cases, deeper thought about your real goals may be required, such as the relief of suffering versus the attempt to restore function.

The opportunity to be with your family today may be much more valuable than the chance for some unlikely extension of life after a long period of alienating medical intervention.

Once you learn the facts of the illness you are dealing with, and you begin to think about your goals, you are ready to:

    ✦ Combine elements to choose treatment possibilities—remembering always that one choice is to do nothing different at this time.

    ✦ Allow the natural course of illness to evolve so that whenever an intervention is chosen, it will be more likely to benefit you than harm you.

✦ Recognize that your goals will often change as conditions change, either as illness evolves, or as complications of treatment occur.

The Interaction of Conditions

Some conditions will evolve slowly over a period of years. Goals at forty are different from goals at sixty, and the same medical conditions may lead to very different treatment choices. Some medical conditions will evolve quickly over a period of months and others rapidly over a period of days. The basic principles are the same, but the emotional shock is usually very different as you see the speed with which your choices change, often for the worse.

Another important element in these considerations is the way the primary illness may be affected by other conditions, either related or unrelated. A broken leg for a patient with a previous stroke may require different treatment choices than a patient with full function to participate in post-operative physical therapy. Similarly, the development of pneumonia in a person undergoing chemotherapy for leukemia represents a different danger and requires different treatment than the same illness that occurs in the captain of a college football team.

This interaction of conditions is always going on at some level. It is one factor that makes real illness in actual people so different from illness described in medical textbooks. It increases the element of uncertainty in complicated disease. It makes the careful establishment of well-thought-out goals very important as a guide in ambiguous circumstances. If circumstances change enough, then goals may have to change, and those goals will continue to reflect our wishes only if we understand why we chose them in the first place.

GEORGE VITALE'S SCRAMBLED EGG

George Vitale had survived an operation for cancer of the larynx 15 years before. He was left with a laryngectomy, which meant he had to learn to speak again by swallowing air and then belching with sufficient control that he could produce soft but intelligible speech. The cigarette smoking that had contributed to the laryngeal cancer had also resulted in a moderately severe emphysema; and although he had stopped smoking at the time of his surgery, he was still left with damaged lungs. I had taken care of his breathing problems and we had been pretty successful. He had moved to Florida a few years before but always came back to New York if he thought something serious was wrong with him.

When he started getting chest pains while taking a walk after dinner at night, he came up to stay with his daughter and made an appointment with a cardiologist. He did not keep the appointment because a severe and persistent increase in the pain heralded a heart-muscle-damaging heart attack and he ended up in the nearest hospital intensive care unit. The crisis passed but he flunked a low level heart stress test. An angiogram was advised. In addition, a chest x-ray was taken while he was in intensive care which showed a spot on the right lung that needed to be explained.

George was transferred to Columbia-Presbyterian Medical Center to see the cardiologist with whom he had originally had an appointment. The angiogram showed severe but treatable blockage of three arteries. After his long history of medical procedures, George was a reluctant and sophisticated consumer. He wanted to know the alternatives to recommendations and what might occur if they did not work. He knew that not every medical procedure worked as doctor and patient wished and he wanted to know exactly what the possible side effects might be. A consummate realist, he explored all the possibilities before giving his consent.

After his angiogram, he was advised to have angioplasty—a process in which narrowings of the arteries are subjected to stretching with a small balloon at the end of a long tube but without opening his chest by actual heart surgery. Other narrowings might be more severe or placed in a position which could not be as easily reached by the tube or cardiac catheter. These would require a more invasive kind of heart surgery. This was obviously of considerably more danger to a patient who had had both a laryngectomy and emphysema.

George made clear that he was consenting to only an angioplasty and that invasive cardiac surgery could be done only in the unlikely event that a complication of the angioplasty required it as an emergency life-saving measure. It could not be done merely because the catheterization team did not succeed at stretching the narrowings. If they failed, he wanted to see how limited his lifestyle might be before consenting to anything more.

Another complication was the spot on his lung discovered on the chest x-ray. A CAT scan was performed to have a better look, and the good news was that it appeared to be a scar from an old bout of pneumonia. The disturbing news was that in examining his liver just under the lung spot, the scan showed some liver spots that could be interpreted as cancer. To be sure of the nature of these spots, a liver biopsy would have to be performed. This involved passing a long skinny needle through the ribs, under the lung, into the liver and then sucking back some of the liver tissue so that it could be examined under a microscope. Usually this is a safe and frequently performed procedure but it becomes much more hazardous when the patient has emphysema and cannot hold his breath well without a larynx. At this point, George called a halt.

"Look Doc. I'm not going to let you do this test to me. If you find that I have cancer, I have too many things wrong for you to do anything about it. Even if you found that I had cancer, you couldn't really tell me how

long I had to live—and I feel fine now. Why should I
take the chance of having a collapsed lung from this
biopsy when the results aren't going to change anything? If you don't find cancer, you are just going to
assume that you didn't hit the right spot and you are
going to want to do it again. No way! I am going back to
Florida before something else shows up. But thank you
very much for fixing up my heart."

Choosing to Do Nothing

George showed a great deal of intuitive wisdom in his choices. He had a positive outlook. He wanted to live as long as he could
and as unfettered by limitations as possible. He was also a realist.
He did not believe that I or my colleagues were magicians. He knew
from experience that we would do anything possible to help him,
but we could not unscramble an egg and if things had proceeded
too far before we had a chance to intervene, that intervention would
be more destructive than helpful.

The word cancer did not frighten him. He had had cancer and
it had been cured. He knew that cancer was not a single disease and
he was more interested in the specific implications for him. He knew
that if there were several spots on his liver and these were cancer,
then the chance of cure was most probably gone. He felt well and was
not going to choose a course of treatment that would make him feel
sick. So it really did not matter at that moment what those spots were.
Had George been in better health, younger, with a family depending
upon him for financial and emotional support and instead of several
spots had there been only one and that in a location amenable to
surgery, then his decision might have been different.

Here we have seen another example of our paradigm of medical decision-making. First, George gathered information. Upon
feeling chest pain, he got a diagnosis which was quite secure on the
basis of his heart attack. He learned that the natural history of the
condition with medication had a reasonable expectation of extended life but that, with some interventions, life might be lived with

less limitation. He knew that other people with his diagnosis were not susceptible to treatment with angioplasty while others were.

Next he established the goal of increasing the quality of his life if this could be done with acceptable risk. In considering treatment alternatives, he would agree to the relatively small risk of angioplasty but not to what would have been, in his medical state, a much higher risk from bypass surgery. In addition, he accepted that as conditions evolved there would frequently be the necessity to change his goals. He was aware that if a rare complication of the angioplasty should occur, he might have to choose among treatment options that he currently rejected.

The other example of medical decision-making George faced was more complicated. This involved deciding what to do about the abnormality found by accident on the CAT scan which was done to evaluate the unexplained shadow on George's chest x-ray. Here there was no secure diagnosis. George's previous medical history altered the risks of the liver biopsy. This diagnostic procedure which carried modest risks in other patients would have a markedly increased risk for George.

In setting up the paradigm, George made two different assumptions. One assumption was that the shadow on the CAT scan had no more importance than the shadow on the chest x-ray, and that there was no risk in ignoring it. In this case, there was no cost attached to foregoing the biopsy while there was considerable risk in submitting to it. The contrary assumption was that the shadow was real and significant—that the shadow was, in fact, an indication of cancer, either arising anew in the liver or having reached there after starting somewhere else.

At this point, George had to seek information about the natural course, likely outcome and treatment alternatives attached to the different types of cancer that might be found. He learned that there was no curative program although some regimens might extend life in patients who had a favorable response. Since he was not having any symptoms and all the chemotherapy programs had very significant side effects, he had no reason to submit to any chemotherapy.

This choice was predicated on his setting goals which valued quality of current life over the increased length of a more wretched existence. Since there was no diagnosis which would persuade George to undertake therapy, any risk attached to making a diagnosis would be greater than the benefit to be derived from making that diagnosis. With his goals in mind and with the understanding that if things changed he would rethink his course, George chose the treatment alternative of doing nothing.

Knowing Which Questions to Ask

Ordinary, intelligent people can make use of the medical decision- making paradigm to help them choose the treatment alternatives which will best reflect their values. George was not a college-educated executive. He had never finished high school and supported his family as a skilled construction worker. Yet he had learned what questions to ask and he wasn't afraid to ask them. He knew that I put on my pants one leg at a time just as he did and he saw no reason to be intimidated into a choice because he might not understand some of the big words thrown at him. Either the doctor could explain the words or he would search for a doctor who would. George was an experienced person. He understood that not every plan worked out as expected and he allowed for that in his work as he did in his medical adventures. He was grateful when things worked well and realistic when they did not.

George knew that when otherwise well planned undertakings do not go as planned it is usually because some important variable has been ignored. When this happens in medicine, it usually pops up as an associated disease which was not given sufficient weight.

**Symptoms and diseases do not occur in isolation.
They are found in people who have medical histories
of previous illnesses and often other physical limitations.**

Although in George's case we have been analyzing courses of action from the point of interaction of several coexistent illnesses—

laryngectomy, emphysema, heart disease, possible cancer in the liver—we could just as truthfully have been analyzing a course of action as a single disease progressed.

SAM WESCOTT'S QUALITY OF LIFE

Sam Wescott had had a laryngectomy just like George and for the same reason. A year after Sam's laryngectomy, a chest x-ray showed a spot on the lung and an examination of it by CAT scan made it look like cancer. The location of the spot determines whether it might be possible to remove it without destroying too much lung tissue. The amount of functioning lung tissue removed would be very important because Sam already had a breathing deficiency from his emphysema. Any lung tissue removed would make him more short of breath and more limited in trying to live his life. If we could have removed a lobe of the lung or even a smaller segment, then this might be a reasonable course of action. If it would require the removal of a whole lung, then it is unlikely that Sam could have survived, even if the cancer had been cured.

If curative surgery would have required the removal of a whole lung and this would have been a fatal blow in itself, a different course of action would have been necessary. After all, we believed that we had found Sam's cancer before it had spread, so he and we had been anxious to treat him as vigorously as possible. Our next choice might have been to try radiotherapy (x-ray treatments) or some combination of radiotherapy and chemotherapy. Each would have its own side effects but these would be less than removing a whole lung in a man with emphysema. Our choice of treatment would also be influenced by our belief about the nature of the lung cancer. Was this a new development which occurred because of the same factors that had caused the laryngeal tumor? Or, was this spot a spread from the laryngeal tumor which had been present but unseen at the time of the operation and now, a year later, had grown large enough to see?

The location of the spot was in the right upper lobe of the lung and Sam's surgery successfully removed the tumor with only that lobe. The appearance of the cancer under the microscope was confusing. It looked like the laryngeal cancer, but the location was more typical of a new lung tumor and we hoped we had cured a second new cancer.

Unfortunately, a chest x-ray nine months later showed a spot in a different part of the lung. The previous surgery had resulted in a diminution of functioning lung tissue as well as a patient who was more short of breath, but still alive. The same would have been true if we had chosen radiotherapy instead of surgery.

The discomforts of surgery, radiotherapy and chemotherapy are not trivial. There is pain, weakness, nausea, shortness of breath, among others. With each round, Sam had been a little less sure that the result was worth the price to him in these discomforts. With each round, his ability to manage his life had been further restricted by shortness of breath. By now, he could just about get from the bedroom to the dining room of his small apartment. He watched the Mets on television because he could not get to the ballpark. Visiting his daughter in the country required wheelchairs, oxygen tanks and breathing supplies. He had lost the spontaneity of simply deciding to get in the car and make a surprise visit.

When faced with a choice of more lung destruction or the side effects of chemotherapy, Sam decided to do neither. His life was barely tolerable as it was. If he lost more breath, his life would be truly intolerable even if he should survive. The weakness from the chemotherapy would be as bad as the breathlessness from the lung destruction. Neither would improve his life. Each would take away from the quality of that life. If he did nothing, at least he would not be worse right away. Maybe the spot is not a cancer. If it is a cancer maybe it will grow very slowly. Sam did not give up hope but he did not take any more surgery, radiotherapy or chemotherapy either. He was quite clear that those modalities of treatment would destroy the quality of his life, and if he did nothing maybe something would happen which would allow him to at least keep what he had.

Our study of George's and Sam's stories has demonstrated some important principles.

**A decision to proceed with vigorous treatment
is appropriate at the beginning of most illnesses,
but you are not obligated to continue with the
same vigor until the patient dies.**

The patient may decide that the cure is not worth the physical or emotional cost to him.

Other previously subsidiary goals may become primary goals. To breathe becomes more important than merely to be alive. To die in one's home in the company of one's loving family may have a higher priority than to remain alive in the midst of a proliferation of tubes and wires in an ICU. These treatment decisions are made every day. Reversals of direction and the appearance of new goals and priorities are appropriate whenever new conditions arise or the results of previous treatment programs are not what was expected.

If we apply our paradigm to Sam's course we see that it helps just as it did in the previous situations. Initially, increasing hoarseness led to an examination by a doctor who saw an abnormality which, on biopsy, proved to be cancer. Other examinations were performed which indicated that the cancer appeared localized. There was no apparent evidence of spread and Sam was a suitable candidate for radical surgery with removal of his larynx or voice box.

At this point, there was a diagnosis which on the basis of the biopsy was pretty secure. There was a further diagnosis that the cancer had not spread. This diagnosis was somewhat less secure because it is usually easier to be accurate in saying that something is present than that something is not present. After this Sam had to learn about the natural course of untreated cancer of the larynx and the likelihood that he would follow this course. The progression of cancer in the throat is painful and obstructs both breathing and swallowing. The usual progression is moderately swift so that Sam would be expected to have serious difficulties in six to twelve months. Sam was otherwise in good health except for a moderate amount of emphysema related to cigarette smoking. There was no other medical condition which was likely either to result in his death before the laryngeal cancer would give him a problem, or to seriously alter his risk with surgery.

Having gathered his information, Sam then had to establish goals. He felt fine and except for his hoarseness was aware of few limitations. He was upset that he would never talk again in a normal voice, but was encouraged when he listened to the way George could speak. If the choice were living with a peculiar voice or dying a painful death, Sam clearly wanted a chance to live longer. The treatment option he chose was radical surgery. His recovery, while difficult, was free of the unexpected until the spot found on the x-ray at his one year check-up.

The appearance of the spot required a whole new medical decision-making paradigm. Information gathering was, once again, the first step but the information was going to be less secure than the first time.

While the CAT scan pointed to a cancer, it is not as accurate as having a biopsy to examine under the microscope. More importantly, the question of whether this was an extension of the first cancer or a whole new cancer had very important implications with respect to natural course.

Cancers which have spread to one new area are generally presumed to have spread to other as yet unseen areas as well. Therefore, the approach to treatment is less generally surgical and more likely to be either chemotherapy or radiation, both of which cover a larger area. There could be no confident judgment about this point until after the spot was removed. As it turned out there was still confusion at that time.

Natural course could not be predicted accurately, and this made the choice among treatment options less clear even if the goals remained the same.

To some extent the choice of treatment was made by the location of the tumor. Despite the underlying emphysema, the removal of a lung segment was likely to cause less loss of breathing capacity that the intensity of radiation that would be required for an equivalent chance of eradication. Sam's goal remained length of life, since he had not yet experienced a serious limitation of his ability to move around. Consistent with his goal, Sam chose surgery again.

The appearance of the second spot found a very changed Sam. He had survived the second surgery but with severe limitations. Information gathering appeared more secure, indicating that this spot was a spread from either of the previous cancers. The natural course suggested that this was now an inexorably progressive illness, although the tempo of decline was uncertain. Most importantly, having experienced seriously disabling limitations, Sam was no longer prepared to trade a more wretched present for a possibly longer life. His treatment choice was at that moment to do nothing different. He felt that all courses of action would result in a deterioration of his quality of life. The evolution of the illness had resulted in his changing goals.

Expecting the Impossible

Despite changing goals as a medical situation weakens, rarely does anyone truly lose all hope. No matter how desperate the situation, no matter how sophisticated the understanding of the patient, everyone waits for the miracle. I have seen this in agnostic physicians and faithful old clergymen. While their rational minds say that the end is near and they may be composed in that knowledge, there is an area of the psyche that still expects the impossible to occur. A physician who leaves her patient no crack through which the light of hope can shine robs herself of the collaboration of her patient. However, many physicians, particularly younger ones, feel this is lying to a patient and a corruption of the scientific precision for which they strive.

If you look at medical problems as jigsaw puzzles for which there is only one solution, adding the uncertainty of hope spoils that precision. But the real world is not a two-dimensional picture. We are not billiard balls being moved about in space by the force of the cue. The dimensions of hope and expectation are very real motivating forces for human endeavor. We get up in the morning because we have things to accomplish, not just because our spouses push us out of bed. The same scientist who tries so valiantly to explain phenomena in mechanistic terms is the purest example of the motivation of hope. As he does an experiment or reviews someone else's data, he hopes that he will find the clue or see the pattern that will unlock the mystery he is exploring. He is being pulled along by that hope—not just being pushed by the wind.

Allowing the patient that small measure of hope often gives her the strength to endure pain, nausea and the uncertainty of the outcome with a natural dignity. It makes her a legitimate collaborator in the event—the physician brings the science and the patient brings the hope.

We have seen some of the ways people respond to illness both physically and emotionally. The value of our paradigm has been demonstrated in those illnesses, both simple and complicated. We have watched goals change as medical conditions change, sometimes over years and sometimes over months. If this sequence of events is telescoped in a time scale to a single hospitalization, the same principles are still valid.

ROSE'S LIMITED LIFE

Rose was a 76-year-old woman with mild hypertension and great anxiety. Nevertheless, when she developed a case of influenza during the annual epidemic and then complained of chest pain, I was the one who developed anxiety in her behalf. She immediately came to my office and an ECG confirmed the sounds of heart inflammation heard with the stethoscope. By the time she reached the hospital, her heart rhythm had become very irregular, atrial fibrillation. Her shortness of breath increased and it puzzled us whether this was due to the abnormal heart rhythm, a progression of the influenza or the development of fluid around the heart from the inflammation.

A variety of medicines, oxygen and breathing treatments were attempted with unimpressive results. Consultants were called and divergent suggestions proffered. The oxygen level in Rose's blood decreased to a point that she was too tired to actively participate in her care, but her 78-year-old lawyer husband, David, took over her role despite his great worry about her obvious deterioration. While the question of thinning her blood to reduce the risk of clot formation was discussed, Rose declared herself by throwing a large clot from her heart to the dominant side of her brain and suffered a large stroke. The debate had centered about the relative risks of clot formation versus the risks of massive bleeding into the inflammatory fluid around the heart. Each development would be potentially fatal, surely incapacitating.

The emergency treatment of the stroke involved the use of an endotracheal tube placed in Rose's windpipe, attached to a mechanical ventilator breathing machine to assure her an adequate supply of oxygen. Rose had walked into the hospital under her own steam and everybody felt that a vigorous approach was appropriate.

Although Rose had signed a "living will" saying that she did not want to be subjected to a mechanical ventilator if there were no reasonable expectation of recovery, her breathing trouble at the onset of the stroke could not be confidently asserted to be irreparable. David who had been appointed "health care proxy" and shared Rose's feelings about artificial life support systems agreed that the uncertainty about the severity of the stroke did not qualify for the withholding of aggressive treatment. The shock of understanding that the stroke would forever change Rose's life weighed heavily on David. He could not really imagine how she would adapt to an invalid life, but they had been married a long time and had faced many trials together. They were far from rich but they had some financial resources and their married children lived nearby and played an active role in their life. David hoped that Rose would agree that even a more limited life would be worth living. He hoped that she would be able to find satisfaction in a ratcheting down of the mobility of her life.

Progression of illness does not occur in a straight line. Generally it occurs in a step-wise fashion. There is a decline and then a slow return toward baseline function.

This allows the patient to appreciate the improvement and, because of it, to become satisfied with a lower level of functioning than she would ever have thought herself capable of accepting. As we have mentioned, people have a great capacity for hope. They also have a great desire to live. When she develops a serious illness, the greatest change in a patient's ideas occurs in the level of disability with which she becomes willing to live. The patient no longer able to walk takes pride in being able to feed herself. The patient no longer able to feed herself takes pleasure in just being able to swallow when fed.

Adjusting to the reality of these limitations is a very different issue from the questions that Sam and George faced in rejecting types of therapy which would decrease an already limited level of function. Neither man was willing to trade a diminution of today's function for a perhaps longer life at a more reduced level of function. However, neither man was unwilling to continue life at the level to which he had been restricted.

The point at which the provisions of a "living will" kick in are when the patient can no longer participate in thinking life at all, or the institution of therapy would prolong a painful or unconscious existence with no reasonable hope of recovery. The definition of a life support system needs to be spelled out in some detail so that the patient and the appointed health care proxy are in accord about the meaning of the instructions.

In New York State the current provisions require that the document state that the patient and the health care proxy have discussed the patient's wishes about artificial feeding and hydration. It need not state what those feelings may be—just that the issue has been discussed. I usually ask patients who have signed living wills to come into my office with their health care proxy so that we may all discuss the implications of the specific instructions.

Even though David was a lawyer and understood the legal aspects of the document clearly, I wanted to be sure that he understood Rose's wishes and vice versa.

Being a health care proxy is not an easy job, and it should not be thought of as a popularity contest. The heavy responsibilities of acting to carry out someone's last wishes puts a severe emotional burden on the person. There is no more eloquent example of this than the beautiful portrayal of Philip Roth's relationship with his father in *Patrimony*. Herman Roth had an inoperable brain tumor. He and his son signed living wills together rejecting the use of life support systems if there were no hope of recovery. Yet at the time that Herman Roth was brought to the hospital emergency room, after he had been in coma for 12 hours, his son was still reluctant to tell the doctor not to put his father on mechanical breathing equipment. He knew that his father had rejected that treatment when he was in perfect command of his faculties. He knew that he himself would reject that treatment if he were in a similar circumstance, yet the knowledge that by his word his father would die sooner was a terrible realization. As difficult as his father might have been in life, he had only one father, and his remaining parent at that.

It matters not at what age one is orphaned.
There is still pain.

However much one may be relieved in the release from pain and suffering of one's parent, the realization that one is now all on one's own is overwhelming. The hesitation that Philip Roth expresses before telling the young doctor that he is not to put his father on mechanical ventilation crystallizes the ambivalence, the pain, the relief and the loss that he feels. The spare prose communicates his love and lament more effectively that the most embellished words. His father has depended on him, and in honoring his father he has accelerated his own loss.

There was still hope amid the devastation for the first two days after Rose's stroke. Any movement of her right side was seen as an indication that it was not as bad as feared. The oxygen forced in by the breathing machine helped support any brain cells that had a chance of survival. Nevertheless, by the third day, it had become clear that the damage was absolute. An emergency CAT scan showed an enormous area of brain involved. Secondary swelling was beginning to amplify the death of brain tissue.

This was unequivocally the situation that Rose had specified in her living will. David had spent most of the time by her side, holding her hand, pleading with her to get better. Their children kept vigil too, each beginning to grieve the loss that was so unexpected. When I brought them the results of the scan and explained its implications, there was a terrible silence. Then Rose's daughter asked, "Does that mean we have to turn off the breathing machine?"

The strict letter of Rose's request would have required the

answer to that question to be yes. However, the emotional burdens of that act are so great that I have never resorted to it or encouraged it. There is enough torment in the ambivalence of not pursuing treatment. To ask someone to live with the memory of disconnecting a loved one's life support system is too cruel. The reality is that a body that is deteriorating irremediably will continue to do this without help.

The only practical requirement of Rose's living will was that once there was no longer a reasonable expectation that she would survive, all further efforts to institute new or alter existing treatment be ceased. This means not adding a new drug if a new type of irregular heart beat occurs or adding an antibiotic if an infection of the lungs or bladder develops. It means not pouncing on her to electrically shock and restart her heart if it should stop. It does mean staying with her, holding her hand and telling her that you love her. It does mean moistening the lips and giving whatever pain medicine may be necessary. It means redoubling the efforts at comfort and discontinuing procedures that may be diagnostic and uncomfortable.

David sat lifelessly in the chair, his son's and daughter's arms around him. He couldn't believe it. His wife had come in with a bad cold and now I was telling him that she would be dead in a few days. Where was his chance to say good-bye? Who would remember with him all the special times and worries that they had shared? He was an old man and soon he was going to be alone.

"Are you sure, Doctor? Are you really sure that this is Rose's scan and there is no mistake—that it isn't someone else's? I just can't..." His chest was heaving and tears escaped his eyes. We clasped hands quietly and I left him with his children. A little while later the son came out and said his father was ready to sign the DNR (Do Not Resuscitate) document which formalized our understanding of Rose's wishes. The next day the fever began and by the following evening Rose's heart had stopped forever.

The rapidity with which the medical circumstances changed in Rose's illness did not alter the validity of our medical decision-making paradigm. The initial information gathering was incomplete as complications developed. Instead of following a typical natural course, Rose veered onto a far more fulminating track. The previous most likely outcome was quickly superseded by a succession of increasingly terrible, if rare, complications. Each one required a new and more precise diagnosis; yet medical decisions often had to be made before all the new information was complete.

The initial goal of restoration to normal life changed to restoration of some functioning life to the goal of not prolonging the dying. The conclusion to which George and Sam had been allowed to adjust over years and months, was thrust upon Rose's family over a matter of hours.

Same Goals; Different Time Scales

The stories of George, Sam and Rose illustrate the same evolution of personal goals on different time scales. At first, there was a commitment to total restoration of function with a vigorous attack on the initial medical problem. However, with each complication came a reassessment of goals and priorities. With each reassessment came a change in the degree of medical intervention that the patient would permit consistent with that change in goals.

The change in goals dictated a change in acceptable treatment options. At no time did any of these patients decide not to live. In each there was the persistence of hope that things would at least stay the same for awhile.

In each there was the willingness to accommodate to a lesser level of function than would have been accepted at the beginning of the illness. Even in Rose's case, she did not make a decision to die. She was unconscious when David followed her instructions not to allow any new treatments. The fundamental issues of treatment goals, hope and accommodation to disability were not altered by the duration of the illness whether measured in years, months or days.

You will want to remember that:

✦ Each patient must decide his own goals and the level of disability he can tolerate.

✦ The patient brings his spiritual and emotional values to this decision.

✦ It is the physician's role to provide the education which will allow the patient to apply those values accurately to the situation he faces.

✦ This collaboration can be fostered by the patient if he learns how to elicit information from the physician.

✦ The physician must provide the patient and his family with an intellectual structure on which to arrange the unfamiliar and emotionally highly charged information they are confronting.

CHAPTER SIX

Recognizing Our Common Humanity

Doctors come in all flavors. Some are tall and thin; some are short and fat. Some are old, some are young. Some communicate well; others don't. There is no way to tell by their appearance whether you are going to have an easy time dealing with them in a crisis. As in any relationship, the success of communication depends on the parties involved.

In this chapter we will look at some of the special features of medical communication between physician, patient and patient's family. Earlier chapters have given us some of the agenda of this communication but we need to talk more about the human factors of the participants.

Communication is not just talking.
It also involves listening. If you don't listen,
you will never communicate with people.
You will just end up lecturing them.

This is true of the patient and the patient's family as well as the physician. Sometimes patients and their families come in "loaded for bear!" They have read something in the paper or heard something on television that they think relates to an illness or a symptom they have. They may demand a certain test or medication, sure that it will solve their problem. It rarely does, but I am often astonished by the origin of the failed communication which led to the outburst.

Words and Their Underlying Meanings

Sometimes the failure occurs because people use the same word differently. Doctors use the word "stomach" for its usual anatomical meaning of the collecting pouch at the upper end of the gastrointestinal tract. Many patients will use the same word as a euphemism for bowel. When they refer to "stomach trouble" they mean that they are constipated. Stomach bleeding refers to rectal bleeding. Patients don't consciously mislead their doctors. They believe they are using the word in a correct and clear fashion.

Sometimes the miscommunication occurs when a patient puts greater importance on a word than the doctor intends. "Emphysema" refers to the destruction of lung tissue usually related to cigarette smoking. The word emphysema does not imply either a lot of destruction or little destruction—just the fact that there is some destruction. Many patients believe the word emphysema refers to terminal respiratory insufficiency. A reference to emphysema on a chest x-ray report will cause great consternation when the really important information is the absence of pneumonia or cancer. In more than one case the use of the word "emphysema" has been able to trigger abstention from smoking, which a great deal of previous conversation had failed to achieve.

Another failure of communication can occur if the patient and the doctor are using different categories of explanation for a condition.

A patient may come to a doctor with an unendurable back pain which he can only believe is due to a broken bone or "slipped disk." After a careful examination and x-rays, the doctor concludes that the problem is a very severe muscle spasm triggered by some particular stress the patient has recently come under. The patient leaves the doctor's office angrily complaining that he is going to find another doctor who doesn't think "the pain is all in his head!"

Just as severe stress may trigger a bleeding stomach ulcer in one person, it can trigger an incapacitating muscle spasm in another. The person with the bleeding ulcer can bleed to death which is certainly not "in his head." The patient with the back pain has confused causes and results. The doctor had not presented the information in a way that the patient could grasp. But the patient did not appear to be in a very receptive state either. We can only guess what other factors may have hindered this communication.

Communication requires listening, not only to the spoken words but also to their underlying meaning.

**Communication between patient and physician
is the beginning of a partnership, a collaborative journey
in which the physician's goal is the relief of suffering.**

For the physician to successfully play this role, the suffering must be heard. When a person comes to the office with a broken arm from having fallen, the suffering looks pretty straightforward. The physician's task would appear to be to splint the arm so that it is properly set for healing. Yet what is the real source of suffering if the patient fell as she was fending off a blow from an enraged drunken spouse who was threatening to kill her? Or if she fell on a slippery spot in the kitchen left by her mother with Alzheimer's disease for whom she was caring?

Going Beyond Words

Spirit and attitude. Even the most apparently simple situation may have many layers if the doctor takes the time to look for them. Words alone do not carry the message. The patient's tone of voice, demeanor, and body language all give hints as to whether there is something else going on. Similarly, the physician's role is more complex than delivering the verdict in Olympian tones. How she dresses herself, the spirit of her office, the attitude she takes to the patient's report of suffering all communicate important information to the patient about the doctor's sense of involvement with and commitment to that patient. In less serious circumstances, these aspects of the doctor's communication may be considerably more important than her technical pronouncements.

The human factor. This goes both ways between physicians and patients and their families. The physician's interest verifies the legitimacy of the patient's suffering. It gives that suffering an objectivity which means the patient is not alone. On the other hand, the patient and his family must recognize that the physician is human, too. His words are not divine. He tries his best, but sometimes decisions need to be made before all the answers are in, and sometimes even when they are, the results are open to various interpretations. Sometimes, there is no answer and it means that time will have to pass for either new information to develop or for the condition to resolve without a definitive answer.

The transfer of information. Nevertheless, a large part of the physician's communication does involve the transfer of information. Your primary source for knowledge about all those issues of information gathering that we discussed in chapter three is your physician. Relating the diagnosis and what it means, the cause, the usual natural course of the condition and the likely outcome in the specific patient are all part of the physician's role as educator. Guiding you through a discussion of goals requires serious communication between patient and physician. Learning the risks and implications of the various treatment alternatives and how they may foster or hinder your goals makes real understanding most important.

Providing Moral Support. When spirits flag, the doctor can communicate support to the patient and the family. This is very different from giving false hope or unrealistic expectations. When the patient has chosen a treatment plan on the basis of well thought out goals, those plans will often contain painful consequences, difficult to endure.

There may be times when it appears to the patient or family that a crippling complication has occurred. In reality this may be an expected part of the usual course chosen, not a diversion from that path.

The patient's pain deserves recognition and honest encouragement can be given that the challenge is being met. The treatment may be hard but there is no need to worry that the goal will not be achieved. Obviously, the doctor needs to be candid with both patient and family if a serious complication does develop. If goals need to be reassessed on the basis of new information, the patient needs to know about that new information in a timely fashion.

Sometimes, the patient has been stretched too far by worry about the future, about family or about how much adversity can be endured. The patient may falter in this role. Now, the physician has to step in and help the patient restore that hope. It is the colloquial "will to live."

The physician can sometimes help by emphasizing the spectrum of possible outcomes and the frequent imprecision of predictions.

At other times, emphasizing the overwhelming expectation of success in a particular goal can restore a flagging spirit. No single approach will encompass all situations. While experience and compassion will improve the chance of success, all physicians can expect to encounter occasional failure. But failure in no way precludes trying again, and the next attempt may succeed in restoring hope.

Listener, educator, verifier of suffering and moral support all represent roles of the human dimension in the physician's communication with you and your family. You need to play the corresponding roles to make that communication the free expression of human beings on a common journey.

The evolution of our communication depends on the mutual work that all parties put into it. The depth and candor of that exchange is limited only by your energy and mine.

Seeking Common Ground

In the past, many physicians would justify their reluctance to discuss difficult issues of diagnosis and prognosis (what sickness you have and what is likely to happen to you because of it) by saying that a patient didn't need to know—that he did not have to make any decisions about property or inheritance that would make any difference. This was a terribly patronizing and deplorable attitude. Every conscious person has a need to know and a right to know what the future may be to the extent that it is possible.

No one's existence is so isolated that he doesn't want to say good-bye to someone or something. There are decisions about goals and treatment courses that can only be made if the patient understands the issues and the magnitude of the situation. My personal commitment to giving all patients the tools to understand and choose their own goals is clear. The medical decision-making paradigm has provided these tools for many. Denigrating the validity of the patient's values is not an effective way of engaging him in a collaborative relationship.

Telling a patient she has multiple myeloma, subacute bacterial endocarditis or systemic lupus erythematosis is not an effective way of communicating, even if the patient is a physician. A doctor must provide information detailing the nature of the disease, the name in common terms and what might be expected in the future.

The use of a common term alone, such as pneumonia, conveys a modest amount of information. The word pneumonia indicates an infection of lung tissue. It does not suggest the infecting microbe, severity or associated and modifying circumstances. "Walking pneumonia" is a colloquial name for a generally self-limited infection of young people first described among army recruits. It was called "walking" because the patients did not require hospitalization. While this infection by the mycoplasma organism, a microbe between a virus and a true bacteria, may put the patient to bed it is rarely thought of as life-threatening.

However, the significance of this infection is very different in a 20-year- old Army recruit than in a 68-year-old man with emphysema or a 45-year-old woman receiving chemotherapy for breast cancer. The man with emphysema may not have the reserve lung tissue to withstand the infection. The oxygen level in his blood may drop and he could very easily die of an associated heart condition. The woman may have been so affected by chemotherapy that her immune system is overwhelmed, and rather than being limited to the lung, her mycoplasma infection could spread all over her body. This could cause a circulatory collapse, a clotting disorder, kidney failure and death.

If you are told that the predictions you are getting are precise, be skeptical. None of us has a crystal ball. The future must be described in terms of possibilities and probabilities. Even the percentages of probabilities must be taken with caution; they are at best gross approximations.

Some results are very likely and others most unlikely, but sometimes the outcome is not clear and the patient must share the physician's uncertainty. But the patient cannot if the physician is not candid about that uncertainty and if the patient is led to expect an outcome which is unlikely. Rather than consolidating the professional relationship with a confident authoritarian air, the physician is undermining it with intellectual dishonesty.

The credibility of the professional relationship must be based on honesty. But honesty does not mean cruelty or lack of human compassion.

There is no news which cannot be couched with a sense of hope or at least a simple statement to the patient that the physician is sad to have to convey the news.

Control vs. the Patient's Active Role

By pretending that the intellectual simplifications necessary to advance science truly describe the complexity of our world, physicians can rob their patients of hope and the will to live. Physicians must become comfortable exposing their own vulnerability for their patients' benefit. Often, this is a very difficult job for a doctor.

Many doctors have applied themselves to the study of medicine because of a need to control their fear of the uncertainty of the world around them. Some find their comfort in understanding a limited area in the most minute detail. Others seek to be the guiding force in a larger arena.

Human beings have many motivations in their endeavors. The value of the endeavor is not dependent on the purity of the motivation. Doctors are not necessarily better people than lawyers or teachers or watchmakers. We have a scientific knowledge and experience that can help people but that knowledge does not operate in a vacuum. Its application is colored by the personal, emotional and spiritual values of our patients.

**In order for doctors to serve you,
we have to work to understand our own motivations
and the difference between our needs and yours.**

The issues of control permeate all levels of the relationship between physician and patient. The control of any specific instance does not necessarily belong to either participant. A physician who tries to control everything will give up the benefits of the patient as collaborator. Furthermore, he treads dangerous ground since by asserting his total control he may appear to guarantee results which are beyond his capacity to warrant. The practical effect of this is that when things "go wrong," usually because nature and biology do not operate with mathematical precision, the patient concludes that the omniscient and omnipotent physician has "done something wrong," either through error or inattention. The patient not only feels he has suffered damage but that the damage is a result of the physician's failure to care enough about him. The not unexpected result is that the patient seeks redress by suing the physician for malpractice.

The solution is not for a physician to abdicate all control to the patient. How a doctor presents information and alternatives has a great influence on the choices that you make. The doctor could not force the issue in every case, even if she tried. But she can marshal the arguments so that most patients will make a predictable choice. Patients do depend upon physicians to offer explanations in terms that are relevant to them. This means not only in understandable language but in use of meaningful analogy and metaphor.

A real discussion of alternatives is a collaborative dance in which patient and physician seek the common ground of communication. The physician has to state and restate the information in a sufficient number of ways that the complexity of the matter to be decided is successfully communicated. The patient has to ask questions or restate his understanding of the case in such a way that the physician may judge whether the information has truly been transmitted.

The physician cannot quit until satisfied that the patient really understands. Often this takes a lot of time and sometimes more than one attempt.

Not every situation is difficult. In a previous chapter we talked about Mr. Strong, who was injured in an auto accident. He was able to appreciate the severity of his injury and the need for immediate intervention without feeling that he needed to be educated in the variety of orthopedic hardware that might be used in the solution of his problem. The patient willingly cedes control to the physician. The situation might be different if the injury had resulted in a partial amputation of Mr. Strong's leg and the physician proposed to complete this job. Mr. Strong would be expected to vigorously protest and to require the physician to defend his position more explicitly. He may even refuse permission for surgery and ask for another opinion.

The request for another opinion often brings the issue of control to a climax. The physician's response can be helpful or an impediment. The security with which he views his own knowledge or approach is an important determinant. So is the security of his own self-esteem.

The more confident the physician and the more secure he is in his opinion, the more helpful he is likely to be in assisting his patient obtain another opinion.

There are times, however, when the physician may feel that despite a sincere effort on his part, the patient has not understood the issue either because of a failure on the physician's part or a psychological block on the patient's part. Here the physician may be the one to suggest another opinion. Or he may feel that the patient's approach is so incompatible with his own values that he can not continue to serve as the patient's physician.

The issue of control represents a complexity in the relationship between patient and physician during the course of illness. In general, I have found that allowing the patient to control low priority areas ensures a greater collaboration and cooperation when more serious issues arise. The patient realizes that we are true team members and will then be more willing to follow if I have to urge a course of action very strongly.

There is also the factor of time in the passing of control. At the onset of an illness the patient and physician have an identical interest, to make as precise diagnosis as rapidly as possible. The physician has the knowledge to do this and despite some grumbling about inconvenience or discomfort, the patient will usually play a passive role.

As the situation evolves and the patient becomes more specifically knowledgeable about his condition both because of the advancing precision of diagnosis as well as the education provided by the physician, he will want to play a more active role. If decisions relating to choice of surgical as opposed to drug therapy are necessary, the patient must participate more directly. If the initial diagnostic tests indicate an advanced condition unlikely to be cured or if the initial treatments have untoward effects, the patient must make choices about future therapies which may depend upon personal philosophical or religious values. The physician will play an increasingly educational role while the patient may exert a greater control by choosing the general level of intervention. These choices will be examined more fully in a chapter to come on Living Wills.

This pattern of patient-physician relationship is supported by the stories of George and Sam that you read earlier. Each acceded quickly albeit unhappily to the advice that he required surgery that would result in the loss of his capacity to utter normal speech. The rapid acquiescence was dictated by the greater desire to live, to survive what would otherwise be sure death from a cancer that was judged curable. While both alternatives were unpalatable, the choice for each man was clear. However, as each illness progressed the cost of each intervention became greater, measured by further physical limitations of the patient's life. Each finally reached a point where the cost outweighed any prospect of benefit, and the patient refused further intervention.

A patient's fears are generally those of the unknown.
Even if there is a fear of a specific disease name such as cancer,
the fear is greatly amplified by the uncertainty of what that
means in that patient's particular situation.

There are fears of death, pain and loneliness. By addressing these fears directly, by stating simply that we all have these fears and by affirming that she will stand with her patient in difficult times, the physician can forge a therapeutic alliance that will transcend the inevitable setbacks of any decline.

Beyond the discussion of diagnosis and prognosis, the communication of physician and patient is extended with the consideration of treatment plans. The patient, previously passive as the diagnostic phase proceeded under the physician's direction, must now take a more active role. He must at least assent to treatment, even if no choice is appropriate.

There is frequent and often patronizing discussion among physicians about the non-compliant patient. In simple English, this means a patient who doesn't follow the physician's advice or prescription. Why would a patient not follow a physician's advice? The main reason is failure in communication. The physician does not communicate the severity of the situation to the patient—perhaps does not communicate it in words and examples that the patient understands. Or the values and worries of the physician are not shared by the patient. Maybe the complexity of the treatment program is beyond the intellectual or physical capabilities of the patient without some additional assistance.

To someone worried for her immediate physical safety from war or urban violence, the longer-term danger of AIDS seems remote.

The prospect that she might be alive in five years to develop a complication would appear almost a triumph. To someone concerned with staying on the job to support his family, the long-term worry of stroke or heart attack from hypertension is less compelling if the medicine necessary to reduce it impairs his ability to work today. The physician has both the luxury and the obligation to take the long view of a problem. But she must evolve a solution in collaboration with the patient which respects the patient's world. The most skillful analysis of a problem is an intellectual arrogance if it is not translated into a practical treatment program.

If the physician is not open to playing the appropriate educational role, the patient may be able to elicit a response by asking pertinent questions:

✦ What is the usual treatment for this condition?

✦ What are the complications or side effects of this treatment?

✦ What other possible treatment approaches are available and what are their side effects?

✦ What is the possible consequence of doing nothing more?

These questions should be enough to get the physician engaged in the discussion, but it will be necessary for the patient to have spent some time thinking about her own goals and values. What are your immediate needs? Pain relief? Longer life? To get back on the job?

Independence? The physician can discuss the implications of the patient's choices with her but cannot and should not project his own values and priorities onto the patient. The patient has to do her homework to be a full participant in this relationship.

Each limb of the communication triangle—patient to physician, physician to family, family to patient—represents a different emphasis and responsibility. The most important limbs are the patient-family and patient-physician communications. The physician-family relationship is derivative. It is important when the patient may be transiently or more permanently incompetent. The family acts as the guardian of the patient's values and wishes. It also acts as the patient's advocate and defender versus the institutions which the patient may confront. The family acts to goad and prod the staff to be aware of the patient's needs. He needs a towel, a drink of water; she needs her pain medicine on time. The doctor's advocacy assures a timely diagnosis and a considered treatment program.

The squeaky wheel gets the oil and the patient's family squeaks for the patient when the patient can't.

Comfort in Time of Crisis

An equally derivative aspect of the physician-family relationship is the role the physician plays in comforting the family in times of crisis. The physician's first responsibility is to the patient, to ascertain his needs and assist him to their accomplishment as much as possible. Sometimes the results are unexpected or expected and sad. As the patient declines, family members have to be educated as to the patient's physical needs and capabilities. They need help to understand what the patient can do and what she shouldn't try. They need help in understanding when the patient's needs are more important than theirs and how both sets of needs can often be met together.

SAUL GETS ANOTHER CHANCE

Saul called me from a southern retirement community to which he had moved after retiring from his law practice at age 77. His doctor there had done some tests and told him that he had inoperable cancer of the pancreas and had six months to live. I had last seen Saul about six months before for a check-up when he came into New York on one of his yearly trips. There had been no indication of trouble at that point and I was anxious to learn more about what had been found.

On a routine visit to check his diabetes, Saul's doctor had noted that he looked jaundiced—not just tanned. Jaundice is a yellowing of the skin which occurs when the bile excretion of the liver is blocked by gallstone, tumor or infection as in hepatitis. When it occurs painlessly, it is usually due to pancreatic cancer. If there is little weight loss it can be a small early tumor and may be surgically curable. Saul had not had much weight loss before the tests were started although the clean-outs and liquid diets had induced a pretty brisk weight loss by now.

Saul said he was coming to New York as soon as he could arrange a flight and asked if I could arrange another opinion for him. I did, but I told him I wanted to see him and the x-rays as soon as he got into town. Over the years, I have had a fair experience with patients who have had pancreatic cancer and I know that no one can predict a lifespan at six months. I have had patients die in six weeks and others live for over four years despite our inability to cure them with surgery. I have also had patients who were cured by surgery that looked inoperable by the scans.

When Saul appeared in the office, he looked awful. He was as deeply yellow as a banana skin and he had obviously lost a lot of weight. He was deeply depressed by what he had been told but had survived radiation for a vocal cord tumor five years before and had lived with his diabetes and a urinary condition, so he did not believe that the game was up. On the other hand he was accompanied by Bea, his third wife. He had lost the first two to breast cancer. He knew very well the limitations of even the most skillful medicine.

Despite his appearance the medical examination was otherwise encouraging. The liver was barely enlarged and even with the weight loss, I could not feel any masses (tumors) in his abdomen. The scans were equivocal. There was no obvious extension of the tumor beyond the confines of the pancreas but the position of the tumor and the resolution of the x-ray made the situation uncertain. Saul went to see the surgeon for his second opinion the following morning.

Dr. Logan reviewed the data and examination and agreed that it was impossible to predict the condition before surgery. Surgery would be necessary in any case, and the sooner the better to relieve the obstruction to the bile duct. The longer this remained blocked, the more severe would be the damage to the liver. If it remained long enough the liver might not recover after the obstruction was corrected. Even if the tumor could not be completely removed for cure, the relief of the obstruction would restore Saul's well-being until another complication ensued.

The surgery was scheduled as an emergency the following day. The obstruction was relieved but the tumor could not be removed. The location had provided for a spread of the tumor in a direction undetected by the scans. Saul was groggy after the surgery and was in no condition that evening to understand what had taken place. The next morning I came in to see how he was and talk about the surgery.

"Well, Saul, how are you this morning? You don't look too comfortable." I probed his abdomen and listened to his chest before sitting down in the chair next to the bed. "I spoke with Dr. Logan about the surgery yesterday. He was pretty happy about the way he was able to hook the gall bladder up to the small intestine to get the bile flow restarted. Your color should start to lighten up in a few days." I paused for a few moments to watch his breathing.

"There is something that he wasn't very happy about," I continued. "The location of the tumor. It wasn't quite where it seemed to be on the scan. We hoped to be able to get it all but it wasn't possible. He was able to bypass all the areas where the tumor could obstruct the liver and stomach but he couldn't get it all out. It isn't too big. It looks like it it's growing very slowly. I don't think it will give us any trouble for awhile. Our concern at the moment is for you to get over the surgery and begin to regain the weight you've lost."

Saul listened closely. I had checked when he'd received his pain medicine before I came in. He needed to be as alert as possible when I spoke to him.

For a long time, Saul didn't say anything. He looked past me out the window. Finally, I asked, "Is there anything else you want to know? Is there any question I haven't answered?"

I waited for a reply. Obviously there were lots of questions I hadn't answered, but I couldn't read his mind and I did not know what concerns were most important to him just then. At last, he looked over at me with a thin smile and asked, "When can I get out of here?"

Saul wasn't ready to talk yet. Bea met me in the hall as I was coming to his room to check him again that afternoon. She was worried. She had expected us to cure her husband's cancer. She had brought him 1,500 miles for that. If he was going to die soon, she should have stayed in Florida. She didn't need to be in this unfamiliar place with strange doctors who couldn't do anything more than the doctors at home. She was right.

"Bea," I said, "I'm glad to see you. I am sorry you had left when I came by last night. Dr. Logan told you he couldn't get it all and that's not good, but the size and location of the tumor was not as bad as it could have been. The future is really not too predictable. As I mentioned before the surgery, some people do well for a couple of years even if the tumor is left behind. Others can get very sick much more quickly. We can't be sure which group Saul is in."

"Is he going to die soon?" she asked. "Will he get out of the hospital? Do you think he will get back to Florida? How am I going to take care of him?"

Bea had a lot of the right questions. We had only some of the answers. "Let's go in and talk to Saul," I suggested. "He should hear the answers too." I took her arm and guided her back into the room.

When we walked in, I said, "Saul, Bea is pretty worried about you and wants to know what's going to happen next. I thought it would be better to speak with both of you together. Do you feel strong enough to talk about this now?" Saul grunted assent. Bea and I pulled our chairs near the bed and sat down beside him.

"Right now, our job is to get you out of the hospital. Fortunately, the surgery was not too extensive and Dr. Logan is a very gentle surgeon. On the other hand, you've been suffering from a liver obstruction and malnutrition, at least in part from the tests you went through. This and your diabetes will make healing more difficult. We can't let you go until we are sure that the intestinal connection won't leak. You have to be eating some solid foods so we know that the hook-ups are working properly. It will probably be several weeks before you begin to feel stronger, but if we are satisfied that it is safe for you to leave the hospital, it will be safe for you to go back to Florida. When you get there, Dr. Stephens will take over again, but I will want you to come up for a check in three to six months.

"What happens when you get home is hard to say," I leveled with them. "You are probably going to have to stay at home for a few weeks. I think walking around the condo will be effort enough.

Most of your energy will have to go into eating many small meals, many times a day. You don't need anyone to be with you all the time, but you may need some help to prepare meals and later to accompany you as you begin to walk more.

"It may be hard for you to adjust to this reduction in strength. You have overcome other medical problems in the past but none have been as debilitating as this will be for awhile. You may harbor some feelings that you are dying, but you're not—not now. Your recovery will be hard on Bea too, even though you're the one who had surgery. She is not only going to be worrying about you every minute and anticipating every complication but the amount of extra work will drain her physical energy. There are times she may push you because she so desperately wants you well and times when she, just as desperately, needs help. Don't try to get by without extra help at home. Don't ask Bea to do everything. She may well try and that will not be good for either of you.

"She's going to need to get out of the house and not just to go food shopping. She's going to need to talk to someone besides you and about things other than your recovery. It doesn't mean that she cares for you less. If she didn't care for you so much, this whole business would be less of a strain on her. Our major thoughts and efforts are going to be directed toward your recovery, but Bea has real needs too and we aren't going to ignore them.

I got ready to leave them. "I'll be back tomorrow. You are going to have to get out of bed again tomorrow and I want you to start walking around the room with assistance. Not far, but often. It will help you build stamina. You won't be able to eat yet but Dr. Logan may give you some fluids tomorrow. That's up to him, but he won't be able to tell until he sees you. I have done a lot of the talking today. I hope you will do more over the next few days and tell me what problems I've forgotten."

Saul's recovery became more complicated than anticipated. His weakened nutritional state impaired the healing of his incision, and two days later a small amount of pus began to leak from one end of the wound. The following day the edges of the skin gaped apart and the superficial sutures had to be removed to allow the pus to drain. Fortunately, the intestinal connections healed more securely. Saul was able to eat only small amounts at a time by the time he left the hospital, but it appeared that he could be kept on the road to recovery by liquid nutritional supplements.

The visiting nurse continued to do daily wound dressing changes at home. Bea's concern about her ability to take care of Saul became even more relevant. She already knew that she would have more work around the house but she had not counted in any way on having to play a nurse's role in wound care.

Bea's concern was one part anxiety that she would do something wrong and one part repulsion at looking inside another's body. The latter was the easier problem to solve. There is nothing intrinsically repugnant about the human body. It is more the mystery that stirs the feelings of fear and disgust.

Merely helping the nurse with the dressing changes allowed Bea to observe the wound in a protected, non-threatening environment. With the repeated exposures the novelty of the sight was reduced and Bea could begin to learn how to change the dressing.

This became pretty easy since by the time Saul was allowed home, the wound had sealed itself internally and the only job was to keep the surface clean and moist so that it would continue to heal uneventfully.

Bea and Saul's return to Florida proved difficult as anticipated but without any bad surprises. Bea was able to find a friend, who lived in the same apartment complex, to be with Saul four hours a day. This gave Bea a chance to have lunch with her girlfriends and see a movie so that she did not feel like such a prisoner. Saul complained that the woman didn't do things as well as Bea and was only with him because she needed the money. But Saul knew that if Bea was to have the energy to do all the extra work, she needed time for herself. Saul appreciated the way Bea had learned to dress his wound and preferred to have her do it than even the visiting nurse. Bea took more time just because she was less practiced and this made it less exhausting for Saul.

There was a happy surprise that Bea came to accept gratefully. Saul did not die on time. His wound healed. He regained his weight. After six months he was pretty much back to normal. He still had the cancer and no one could forget that it was slowly growing, but it wasn't causing any trouble right then. Bea and Saul lived in the concrete moment. In each of their previous marriages they had watched spouses get sick without warning and die. Saul's current illness had been like that. Now they had been given a reprieve. It might be a week, a month or a year—maybe longer. But they were going to enjoy it now and not worry much about the problems ahead.

The Mutual Humanity of Doctor and Patient

Among the key features of the patient-physician relationship are information and action.

The physician educates, listens and then acts. The success of his professional intervention does not require him to love everyone he takes care of. He may enjoy helping those he likes.

The physician may play a more complex role in the care of those she likes, but professionalism must transcend this personal affection. Love and emotional support are the role of the patient-family relationship. A problem develops if the patient confuses the role of these different relationships and seeks love from the physician.

What can the patient legitimately expect of the physician in human terms if love is off limits? Arthur Frank writes, in *At The Will Of The Body*, about this question in the context of two serious illnesses which attacked him at the age of about 40. A medical sociologist, Dr. Frank first developed a serious viral infection of the heart. This resolved completely after a period of months and he prepared to resume his normal life, ignoring illness as would any otherwise healthy young man. However, he soon developed a rapidly progressive malignant tumor of his testes. Although he appears to have had an equally successful remission of this disease, he could no longer ignore the role of illness in the course of life. This forced him to confront these issues and finally to write about them with a perception that could come only from personal experience.

Frank's demand is for "recognition." He wants acknowledgement that critical illness is not just a molecular problem. He wants appreciation of the complexity of human existence—that there is a discontinuity of life experience produced by staring into the abyss of critical illness. Life does not just go on as if nothing has happened. The validity of spiritual values and personal relationships are tested with a unique intensity. The patient is engaged in an undertaking whose outcome is very much in doubt. This may be business as usual for the physician, but not for the patient. As Frank writes:

"The staff cannot match the patient's emotional intensity on such occasions, and they should not expect the patient to mimic their professional calm."

The physician who requires an unnatural cheerfulness or display of courage as the price of collaboration will be rewarded with a counterfeit relationship.

Critical illness is critical because the art and science of medicine makes the treatment of these conditions uncertain in outcome. For most people, pneumonia, a urinary tract infection or a broken leg do not represent critical illness today. The appropriate, overwhelming expectation is that one will recover completely. There may be discomfort. There may be inconvenience and annoyance with the disruption of plans, but there is no sense of mortal danger. The science of medicine has mastered the diagnosis and treatment of these formerly frightening conditions.

Critical illness represents what is still a frontier in medical science. Yet the professional challenge to the physician's skill is dwarfed by the personal challenge to the patient's existence.

The physician cannot use the intensity of his own intellectual commitment to ignore the patient's stake in this adventure. No outcome—not even the discovery that the diagnosis was in error—will return the patient to his former innocence. It is this "recognition" that Frank demands.

Frank can understand, accept, forgive the physician's inability to cure him. He can even accept that the physician, through error or ignorance, may provide the wrong treatment. But he is not prepared to accept a physician's refusal to engage him as a fellow human. His pain must be acknowledged. Both psychic and physical pain matter and this "recognition" is the necessary element of the relationship between patient and physician.

The illness is not only "of the patient." The physician shares a role in the way his intervention modifies the evolution of the illness in the patient. The relief of physical pain, the prevention of complications, the possible eradication or alleviation of the initial disease are obvious ways the illness reflects the physician's management.

STANLEY

Stanley had a successful vending machine route. He would drive his truck from location to location resupplying the machines and collecting proceeds. While not glamorous, it afforded him a respectable living and, together with his wife's earnings, they were helping two children in college.

One day, he looked up from emptying a coin box to find himself staring into the end of a snub nosed "Saturday night special." He had been threatened in the past and had twice before handed money over to robbers but he had never had a gun so close to his head. The sudden release of adrenaline made his heart pump so powerfully that he felt it fill his chest. He broke into a sweat and was very light-headed as he returned to his truck. The robber had fled with the money and Stanley was left alone. The surge in his chest progressed to a hot feeling as if a light bulb had been turned on behind his breast bone. He had never had any feeling like this before but he thought he was having a heart attack. He was only 47 years old. He fumbled with the key and was able to drive a few blocks further where there was more traffic and he could hail a cab. He knew that the closest hospital was Columbia-Presbyterian and he asked the cab driver to get him to the emergency room.

The intern's ECG in the emergency room confirmed that he was having a heart attack. The staff swiftly moved to stabilize him and transferred him rapidly to the cardiac intensive care unit. This unit was quite new. Stanley had been stricken some years ago before cardiac units were a technological novelty. When Stanley's family learned of his attack they rushed to the hospital and were delighted to arrange for an internationally respected cardiology specialist to take over his care. The cardiologist came in to examine Stanley and review the records. He questioned Stanley about the circumstances of the event. When he finished, he summoned Violet, Stanley's wife, to the bedside and delivered his opinion.

"Stanley, you have suffered a myocardial infarction. In lay terms, you've had a heart attack. All myocardial infarctions are very serious. You may suffer complications. There may be an arrythmia. You may develop congestive heart failure. You may perforate your myocardium. All of these would be very bad, indeed. Fortunately, you're in our cardiac unit and we'll be able to monitor you very carefully. We'll be able to intervene quickly if something untoward should happen. You'll be under constant observation. When I judge that it's safe, I'll move you to another room for the remainder of your convalescence. When you leave the hospital, it'll be necessary for you to change your life—a lot."

The somber authoritarian air of the old professor

scared Stanley. He had a family, a business and children in college. He sweated under the electrodes taped to his chest. This seemed a lot more dangerous than having a gun pointed at him. Stanley resolved to do whatever the old professor told him to. He did not want to die and he would change his life any way that was necessary.

The period of hospitalization saw a dramatic change in Stanley's personality. Despite his rapid physical progress, he became tentative and meek. He was everyone's favorite patient. He did not complain, he followed orders precisely. He did not ask many questions. He was grateful for anything that was done. When the cardiologist came in for his final visit before Stanley's dismissal, he told Stanley that he must take it easy and not exert himself. He must find a new kind of work since driving and lifting cartons required too great an exertion. While Stanley was making progress, he would have to continue to be careful.

Stanley sold his vending machine route and took a sedentary desk job. He led a quiet life and continued to see his old cardiologist every three months for an examination and an ECG. He never had had any symptoms related to his heart after the hospitalization. The cardiologist would examine him carefully, review the ECG and then announce somberly, "Your heart appears to be stable. Continue to be careful as you've been."

Year after year this ritual was repeated. Each time Stanley left the doctor's office he had a tentative, incomplete sense of relief that he might be fine for another three months. Periodically, some of his old humor would peek through. Almost nine months passed before he had resumed sexual relations with his wife. He did not dare ask the professor, and the professor had never broached the subject.

I first met Stanley some years later when the cardiologist referred him for evaluation of a stomach pain. Stanley related some of his history at that time but I did not really get the whole story until much later. I would see both Violet and Stanley for their general medical problems, which were not frequent. I rarely saw either of them as often as every eighteen months. In fact, I thought of them as the cardiologist's patients whom I would happen to see for less serious problems. However, at one visit, Stanley said, "I think the cardiologist is getting a little old. He's taking longer vacations and I would like to see a cardiologist who might be around more if I need him. Can you recommend someone?"

I replied that I wasn't aware that the cardiologist was retiring. Since Stanley seemed to be in perfectly fine health, I did not anticipate any urgent need. Besides if there were an emergency, since the cardiologist and I practiced at the same hospital, I could always arrange for his admission.

"The truth is that I want a different cardiologist," Stanley admitted. "I had a heart attack almost twenty years ago. I haven't had any symptoms of any sort since. You have examined me many times and never found anything wrong with me. Yet the cardiologist still wants to see me every three months, and after every visit he behaves as if he'll be surprised to see me alive at the next meeting. I used to be afraid but now I'm just mad at having been so frightened. I've been walking around for these 20 years afraid to lift anything or get excited or really live at all. I want another opinion about what I may really have to be afraid of."

Stanley then went into even greater detail about the story just told. By the end, he was expressing himself with a lot of emotion. It was clear that he had been intimidated into behaving as a cardiac cripple with very little justification.

His disease had become an illness owned by the physician rather than the patient. The benefits that the cardiologist may have provided during hospitalization had been eroded by the emotional destruction he had authored in the subsequent years.

Role models serve an important function in professional education. Learning how more experienced practitioners deal with many of the human issues that are never discussed in medical school has helped the professional maturation of all of us.

Nevertheless, I frequently point out to my students that we can often learn as much from negative role models as from positive ones. Seeing something done in a way you never want to repeat can be a far more illuminating experience than ten opportunities to see something done well. However knowledgeable the cardiologist may have been about the mechanical illnesses of the heart, he demonstrated very little knowledge about the people in whom these illnesses were found. He failed every one of the roles that we have spent these pages discussing. I hope that this story will help you find and appreciate the physician who tries to fulfill these functions for you.

You will want to remember:

✦ Communication involves listening as well as talking.

✦ Patient and doctor must define their terms and make certain they are using the same categories of explanation for a condition.

✦ Communication between patient and physican is a collaborative journey in which the physician's goal is the relief of suffering.

✦ It is appropriate to expect to know the spectrum of possible outcomes and the frequent imprecision of predictions.

✦ Doctors often need to work to understand their own motivations and the difference between their needs and yours.

✦ The more confident a doctor is in his opinion, the more likely he is to be helpful in assisting you obtain another opinion.

✦ The squeaky wheel gets the oil.

How does a doctor tell his patient what she has? How does he focus the patient's thoughts to the cure or management of the condition? How does he engage the patient in collaboration about a treatment plan? The patient may live, the patient may die, but a certain part of the impact of the condition on the patient's life will be determined by the physician's behavior. This does not require love or even friendship, but it does require, on the part of both participants, an honest recognition of their mutual humanity.

CHAPTER SEVEN

Illness Creates Complicated Feelings

Our relationships with the people closest to us are very complex. Our parents try their best to raise us well. Things get in the way—like time, money, fatigue and ignorance. How we respond to our parents when we are adults is very much determined by experiences of childhood. We may be parents ourselves but when we talk to our own parents it is as if we were 10 years old again. Our love is tempered by ambivalence, the ability to feel opposite or contradictory emotions at the same time. We may continue to harbor resentments of our parents' shortcomings from our childhood at the same time that we still desperately seek their belated approval.

Sometimes the overt reasons for these resentments have an origin much more contemporary than our childhood, and sometimes the circumstances are less troubled.

JULIE AND HER SON DAVID

David Green had been angry with his mother Julie for a long time. His parent's marriage had not been good almost from the beginning. This was not because of alcohol or infidelity but from fundamentally different approaches to life. Julie grew up in poverty, her immigrant mother working to support her four children after their father had left her for another woman. Despite this poverty his mother had the soul of an artist and always envied her sister who had become a well-known actress.

Julie's artistic soul, however, could not support her any better than her mother had and during the depression she married a steady man from a middle-class family. Her son David's birth created a bond and focus for the marriage where none other existed. The marriage lasted until David graduated from college. Julie had developed a level of financial independence as an executive secretary and, with the end of the obligations of college tuition, she moved out.

When David's father got sick, David bore the brunt of caring for him. He resented this imposition. He had married and was embarking on a career after having served in Vietnam. Why didn't his mother take care of her husband? Why did she leave this to him? Couldn't she see how many obligations he already had? And after watching all those men die in Vietnam, how could he watch his father slowly perish?

After his father died and David closed up his father's apartment, he was damned if he was ever going to talk to his mother again. She left the dirty work to him and he would never let her forget it.

Julie was sorry to learn that her husband had gotten so sick. They hadn't lived together for many years and during most of their marriage there had been little mutual support. Julie had expected financial security but instead found that she had to go to work to help support the family and save money for her son's college tuition. She had supported her mother all those years and taken care of her when she had become invalided by a stroke, until she died. It was hard running to her mother's apartment, then to work, and then to take care of her own home.

When she moved out on her own, Julie felt enormous relief. No longer did she have to worry about anyone else. David was grown and educated. Her husband could take care of himself. There was no one else to whom she was obligated. She had a responsible job where she was appreciated and well paid. Finally she could live like a human being, no longer dependent on anyone else.

When Julie learned that her husband had terminal cancer, she was sorry but decided it was not her problem. She had spent her life taking care of other people but not this time. She was on her own.

Over the next 20 years, Julie had a number of illnesses. Some required hospitalization but none was life-threatening. As she got older and realized how alone she was, she felt more vulnerable. When her income was reduced by compulsory retirement, she became frightened. She often tried to contact David. Usually, David's wife said he was out and would return the call, but he never did. On the rare occasion when he answered the phone, he said he was sleeping and would call her back later, but he didn't. When she tried to call him at work, he reacted so angrily that she never dared try that again. That had been a long time ago.

Julie had developed a tenuous telephone relationship with Priscilla, David's wife. Priscilla had not suffered the emotional devastation of parental separation and did not carry the grudge that David did. Julie was a very lively, well-read and funny lady who could easily pass for many years younger than she really was. It was not hard to be her friend, as long as you weren't her son.

As Julie neared her 80th birthday, the part-time secretarial jobs which supplemented her income became less frequent. The financial crunch made her attempts to contact David more urgent. The car she used to get to her jobs was failing and needed expensive repairs or replacement. Julie needed help and she appealed to David through Priscilla. Surprisingly, there was a response. The negotiations were not smooth. The built-up tensions escaped in suppressed explosions. At last, Julie got the new car but the sputtering relationship with David did not develop any further.

Without warning, Julie called me early one November morning complaining of a strange change of her hiatus hernia pain. As I listened to the description of symptoms, I became more concerned that this was not the development of an ulcer but the beginning of a heart attack. I told Julie to hang up the phone and to open the front door. I was sending an ambulance to bring her to the hospital. In the Emergency Room, the electrocardiogram confirmed my suspicions and showed some ominous extra heartbeats. Julie was rushed to the cardiac intensive care unit as I called a senior cardiologist to take over her specialized care. My next call was to David.

"David," I said, "this is Dr. Postley. I am with your mother in the cardiac intensive care unit at Columbia. She is having a heart attack. There are some dangerous features developing and I think you ought to be here."

"Thanks for calling, Doctor, but it's pretty late and I have some important meetings in the morning. Would you mind giving me a ring in the morning with a progress report?"

"David," I continued, "I did not call you casually. I know that your relationship with your mother has been strained, but she is an old lady and she could die from this heart attack. If she does, her pain will be over but yours will not be. You worked hard to help your father when he was dying. That help was a comfort to him but it also left you with a sense of accomplishment to temper your loss. If your mother dies alone, you will have lost the opportunity to resolve your feelings about her. Those feelings are not all bad."

"Look, Doctor, I know you mean well but this is none of your business. Your job is to take care of my mother and not to be my psychiatrist. If I need one, I'll get one of my own, thank you. I don't wish my mother ill but she wasn't around when I needed her, and I really don't see that I have any obligation to be with her now."

"David, my call was not prompted only by a concern for your mother. I have had experience with family alienation at a time of serious illness. I have seen the effects of having someone die without some reconciliation. My greatest concern right now is getting you an opportunity to avoid this calamity. Please come in and see your mother, much more for your sake than hers."

"Well, Doctor, I'll give some thought to what you say, but I'm not inclined to come in, and I certainly wouldn't advise you to wait up for me."

"Okay, David, you can come in any time and I will let you know if there is any change."

David did not come in that night, or the next. Julie's heartbeat stabilized with treatment and the size of the heart attack stayed small. The outlook for recovery was excellent and there would not be real restriction in her activity once she convalesced. I did not tell her about my call to David. If he came it would be a great boost for her, and if he didn't she would be hurt more by the knowledge that I had asked him.

I did not call David again. I had never spoken to him before. All I knew about him I had inferred from things that Julie had told me over the years. There was so much that I could not know about their relationship. To push him harder might be counter-productive.

When I came to examine Julie the following day, I found her in tears but not sad. "David came to visit me today. He couldn't stay long, he's so busy, you know. It was so wonderful to see him. He said he would come again. I really hope he does."

David did come again a few days later. I don't know what was discussed. Julie was very defensive about David. If her sister or anyone else criticized his behavior she attacked them swiftly. She was tentatively cheerful after his visit. "He seemed so happy that I was getting better. I think he was really afraid that I might die."

Julie went home early the next week. When I saw her for an office visit two weeks later, she let me know that David had called her at home. He did not call again after that, and when she tried to call him he was not at home. Another fledgling reconciliation floundered. However, there had been some thread of communication re-established.

There is the suggestion that had Julie been or stayed sicker, the circumstances to support this reconciliation would have been more favorable. Some foundation for a future relationship has been laid. I hope for David that when Julie develops her final illness, it evolves slowly enough to allow him the chance to reconcile more decisively.

Normal Human Failings

Growing up involves understanding and forgiving your parents their normal human failings. Every child wants a perfect parent and for a long time believes he has one. When the recognition of imperfection finally dawns, the extent of that failing is increased by previous veneration. The sense of betrayal at this discovery fuels the tempest of adolescence. Likewise, relationships among brothers and sisters as adults often repeat the struggles and conflicts of childhood.

All of these complicated feelings are amplified and focused at a time of medical crisis. The illness of a mother will stir different feelings than the illness of a brother or wife or child. Your psychological needs are usually very different from those of the person taken ill. Recognizing and reconciling these divergent needs adds more stress. The divergence of these needs is not an indication of self-absorption and selfishness. It may result from a deep concern for the other. But it may also result from erroneous assumptions about the other's needs. In O'Henry's short story "The Gift of the Magi," husband and wife each give up something in order to acquire a gift for the other. But each gift was made unusable because of what the other had already given up. This is not uncommon in human relationships. The solution is communication.

What to Do and Not to Do

Our understanding of the communication between patients and families at the time of medical crisis includes both what to do and what to avoid.

The sequence of things to be done:

✦ Affirm support
✦ Seek information
✦ Assess needs
✦ Most important, communicate love.

Affirm Support

The family's first real response should be the affirmation of support in a time of crisis. This is not the time for sibling rivalries to be replayed although they often are. Parent-child tensions that have been dormant for years may suddenly be revived. There is plenty of time to work out these issues later. To focus on them at the beginning will only complicate the necessary evolution of communication. Make no mistake, this evolution of communication is crucial for everyone involved. Critical illness is a significant event; the outcome is uncertain. The patient may die. If she does, the people around will have to live with their responses and actions. If she lives, there may be many changes in her reactions to others and there may be a chance to rebuild a relationship that has been troubled. Seize the opportunity!

When learning about a critical diagnosis, the patient is afraid. Tell him you love him and will stand by no matter what. Let him know he is not alone.

There are many patients for whom the disclosure of a critical diagnosis is emotionally very disorganizing. Instead of beginning to plan a strategy of action, they may do something completely different and strange: clean the house, polish the silver, paint the garage. These are really not so strange. This sudden introduction of uncertainty disrupts the orderly flow of the patient's life. By doing something to create order in one corner of his life, he is trying to deal metaphorically with this perturbation.

Seek Information

You can help. After affirming your emotional support, help the patient seek information. This may not be easy. Because the patient feels so vulnerable, any confrontation of authority may appear to increase the uncertainty of his existence. Done properly this can be avoided.

Go to the doctor with him and ask these questions:

1. What's the diagnosis? Is there a common name for this?

2. How did you arrive at this diagnosis?

3. Is there still the possibility of any other diagnosis?

4. Are you a specialist in this condition?

5. Can we arrange a consultation with a[nother] specialist for a second opinion?

These are not hostile questions and no physician should object to their being asked or to answering them. In fact, the physician may welcome the chance to discuss the disease in these concrete terms. This is the way she thinks of disease professionally and rather than feeling challenged she may appreciate the opportunity.

More often a doctor confronts a confused and emotionally upset patient with whom it is very difficult to communicate any information. When there is serious news to be delivered, most experienced doctors know the patient will not be in a position to make a decision about treatment course at once. There is too much to assimilate. The patient needs time to digest both factual information and emotional significance. Often another appointment is scheduled to review the situation and plan the treatment, especially if surgery is a consideration.

This is a perfectly appropriate time for another family member, or more than one, to accompany the patient and participate in the discussion. But do your homework. Read something about the condition in any of the good home medical advisers that have been published, such as one published by Columbia University, but there are others. Do not waste time—either the physician's, the patient's or your own.

The topics and emotional range of communication between

patient and family will evolve over the course of an illness just as it does between patient and physician. The initial tendency will often be to minimize the danger of the situation, as if giving words to the unspoken fears make their reality more likely. The first mention of a dangerous diagnosis will often evoke disbelief and denial even from patients who, in the past, may have anticipated disaster with the appearance of each new symptom.

Alternative explanations, sometimes very far-fetched alternatives, may be proffered by patients who are obviously aware that something very serious is wrong. The patient who has hidden a large festering breast cancer from the physician's examination may insist that her back pain is due to taking too many vitamins. Another patient may blame a "chronic cold" for the bloody sputum of a lung tumor. The family may engage in a certain emotional collusion with the patient in this denial. The sudden revelation of serious illness is shocking. Family members may anticipate loss of the companionship, love and support of the patient. They may harbor guilt about belittling the significance of early symptoms that the patient had reported.

Assess Needs

Almost as important as what to do is what to avoid:

✦ Don't waste your time trying to affix blame.
✦ Help the person who needs help.
✦ Do not guarantee an outcome.

Serious illness, by definition, defies guarantees. As we shall see, getting caught in that trap harms you more than the patient.

Not infrequently, this is a time for trying to affix blame. The family may blame the patient for not reporting the early symptoms when they first occurred or they may blame the patient for having engaged in behavior, smoking or diet which contributed to the illness. The patient may blame the family for not taking the reports of the early symptoms seriously. The family or the patient may blame the doctor for not making a diagnosis in a more timely fashion.

There is often truth in at least some of these claims, but usually not a great deal of relevance. To try to dissipate the fear of illness by affixing such responsibility perpetuates unnecessary division at a time when mutual support is much more important. Such behavior can amplify the tensions of childhood family relationships.

Sometimes you may feel that the patient has "cried wolf" before and that you have been suckered into believing it. You are angry and embarrassed by the experience. You have sworn never to let it happen again. Forget it. I have never been embarrassed to be "suckered."

**I would rather be thought a fool
than not help someone in need.**

Of course, if I realize that the patient's interpretation of symptoms and realities are different from my analysis, I will not be hesitant to address this. Perpetuating inaccuracies of understanding or emotional misconstructions are not in anyone's interest.

If you are skeptical about a diagnosis reported by a mother who has exaggerated in the past, express your distress for her condition and suggest that you go to the doctor with her to better understand the situation. This can serve many purposes. You are showing solidarity with a parent who feels some sense of abandonment, however unjustified. You are making a personal contact with the doctor which may provide you with more easy access in the future. Finally, there may really be something serious developing, and anticipating future needs will allow you to plan for them.

There are some responses that occur in families getting along as well as in those disturbed by tensions. A child, spouse or sibling may feel it is her responsibility to "make everything alright." This can be a destructive attitude. You did not give the patient the illness and, except in the unlikely event that you are the world authority on that particular disease, you are not in a position to effect a cure.

Just as the physician can jeopardize her relationship by appearing to guarantee a cure, you too can strain your relationship with the patient. There is a big difference in the nature of this strain, however.

While the patient may resent the physician for failing after assuring success, the patient will not feel that way about a family member because the patient has never believed that a family member had the capacity to cure. Nevertheless, the relationship may be strained because of a sense of inadequacy. As a member of the family, you may subconsciously feel you have guaranteed a result that you cannot really deliver. Avoid this emotional trap from the beginning. Your role in this is not to practice medicine but to be a moral support to the patient.

Rather than exaggerating the severity of illness, a patient will sometimes omit any mention of a serious diagnosis. This is rare in spouses, but a single parent, living alone, may do this. In some cases, this is because there is infrequent communication to begin with. In others, the patient may believe he is sparing the child unnecessary worry or that there is some stigma attached to illness. None of these is a good reason. If you are the patient in these circumstances, don't do it.

If you think it will serve your child right for ignoring you, think again. That child may have taken your support for granted and could not imagine that you would ever need him.

If he now sees a positive role to play he may surprise you with his enthusiasm. Give him a chance. It may give both of you the opportunity to rebuild a relationship.

If you think you are sparing your child worry, you are not. There will be no less worry, but there will be greater hurt at having been excluded from your confidence. There may be anger at having been thought too immature, unstable or inconsequential to be trusted with the information. The caring child will be more upset for not having been given the opportunity to provide help and emotional support from the beginning.

Do not waste time and emotional energy worrying about any stigma of disease. Kidney cancer is no cleaner than heart disease or lung cancer. Your concern and your family's concern should be for the future. What are you going to do about it? How advanced is the condition? What are your treatment options? How are you going to choose among them?

Most diseases have some component of patient contribution—some witting and some inadvertent. Lung cancer is highly correlated with cigarette smoking. Most patients with lung cancer have been heavy smokers, but some patients with lung cancer have never smoked and most people who smoke do not get lung cancer.

The fact of lung cancer does not make you a bad person.
It may make you an unlucky person or a foolish person,
but the fact of illness is a reality which is independent
of any consideration of stigma.

The issues of advanced lung cancer are quite similar among patients, unrelated to whether they smoked or didn't. Is the smoker who doesn't get lung cancer any less innocent than the smoker who does get lung cancer? If you are suffering shortness of breath and bone pain from lung cancer, there are concrete problems that need to be addressed. How they are addressed does not depend upon whether the patient was a smoker.

A patient's behavioral contribution to illness is only one component. There are genetic contributions and environmental contributions. The young man with familial hypercholesterolemia from both sides of his family will likely get coronary artery disease no matter how careful he may be about his diet, smoking and exercise. The young woman with lymph cancer because she grew up in a house with a polluted water supply and the man with AIDS contracted from the blood product treatment of his hemophilia are equally unlucky.

But what about the housewife with AIDS which she contracted from her husband, or the gay man with AIDS contracted before the means of transmission was understood? They too are unlucky. Women have sex with their husbands all the time without contracting AIDS and there are large numbers of gay men who have had sex without contracting AIDS. We are responsible for ourselves and for assessing our risk factors.

**It is up to us to minimize risk factors in our lives,
but there is always some area that we cannot control.
The uncontrollable factor will be genetic in some,
environmental and accidental in others.**

People are human and imperfect. We may have the knowledge to prevent disease. We may in fact most usually behave in a
way to prevent disease. But not always. And when we don't we
may get "caught."

To begin assessing blame and attributing stigma is irrelevant by
the time serious disease develops. Stigmatizing a patient will not
make the disease go away. It will not make it any more responsive to
treatment. It will not make the chemotherapy or surgery easier. In fact,
it is likely that it will make everything worse. It will delay diagnosis
and treatment. It will amplify the pain of surgery and the side effects
of chemotherapy. It will inhibit the emotional alliance with family.

Communicating Love

This is the time for supportive communication. Anything that
disrupts this communication will only complicate the course of any
illness. The time to apply pressure to the patient's behavior is when
there is still the chance of preventing disease—not after it has
already developed. Punishing seriously ill people by isolating them
emotionally or restricting their medical care is shameful.

The family's crucial job in serious illness is to provide emotional support and love. All the petty interferences of life need to be
put aside and the ranks close. The emotional support can be vocal,
out loud, or just holding someone and telling them they are not
alone. It is easy to misinterpret communication that is not spoken. I
would advise that you say out loud what you mean.

Do not depend on the worried sick person to read your mind.
Do not minimize the severity of the illness even if this makes you
uncomfortable. It is much worse for the patient who has heard the
bad news and is staring into the abyss, uncertain of the outcome but
knowing the danger she faces.

**Facing illness alone is a thousand times worse than
knowing that someone who cares is standing with you.
Only you can let the patient know you are there.**

No doctor can or should be expected to provide the intensity
of emotional support that a family can. But family members will
have to resolve some of their own differences by true communication
if they are going to be able to provide that support. They will
have to deal realistically with what is.

At a time of medical crisis, the patient's agenda is love, fear
and hope: the love of his family, the fear of the unknown and the
hope that some path can be found be found to safety. The doctor can
provide the medical information, guidance and treatment, but only
the family can give the mainstay of support that literally makes the
difference between life and death.

You will want to remember:

✦ Our relationships with the people closest to us are complex.

✦ Human emotions are amplified and focused at a time of
medical crisis.

✦ It is essential to affirm support, seek information, assess
needs and, most important, communicate love.

✦ Blame and guilt surface quickly and serve only to perpetuate unnecessary division at a time when mutual support is
far more important.

✦ Sometimes doctors misunderstand their patients; and
families, their loved ones.

✦ This is a time for supportive communication. Anything
that disrupts communication can only complicate the course
of any illness.

✦ It is easy to misinterpret communication unspoken.
Whatever you mean, say it out loud.

CHAPTER EIGHT

From Ambivalence to Forgiveness

The tensions of normal family life are complex. Intense feelings generated by experiences in childhood and even infancy continue to color these interactions into old age. The attractive and repulsive forces of sibling relationships are often amplified at times of a family crisis such as medical catastrophe.

Most children think that a brother or sister was favored over them, if not in general, at least with respect to some important event. Even if the favoritism is not true, the fact of the belief is an important foundation for later sibling discord. Conversely, the shared experiences in which the family acted together provides a basis for positive family forces. Every life will include an alternation of bonding and divisive events. Each participant will probably appreciate the same event in somewhat different terms. Often a person is able to appreciate an event in both a positive and a negative manner.

The Opposing Forces of Ambivalence

The child who breaks his right arm falling off his bicycle suffers the pain but enjoys the thought that he won't have to do any school homework until the cast comes off. He's in pain, but he's happy. Two objects may not be able to occupy the same physical space at the same time, but two thoughts—even opposing thoughts—may and often do occupy the same mind at the same time.

This is what we call ambivalence—harboring conflicting thoughts about an event, person or idea in a single moment.

If we like playing ball but hate practicing the piano, this is not ambivalence. We like playing ball. Perhaps we practice the piano because our mother required it and we knew that if we did not, we would not do well in the piano recital. The reasons we agree to practice the piano have nothing to do with the piano; they have to do with our loving our mother and wanting to avoid shame at the class recital.

Ambivalence occurs when we feel conflicting thoughts about the same thing at a single time. It is the combination of feelings that we have when we see a squirrel that has been run over in the street. We may feel a terrible attraction to see it close up and yet be equally repelled by the disgusting sight. We must entertain the two feelings simultaneously. This ambivalence reflects the complexity of human emotional life.

It is difficult to put in a picture or a diagram. Can you imagine an automobile that is painted wholly red and blue at the same time, or a spoon that is both hot and cold at the same time? The physical world defies what can be appreciated by the emotions. The conflicting emotions you feel when your older brother beats you by a humiliating score in the club tennis finals only begin to illustrate the concept of ambivalence.

In Chapter 4, we read about the dilemma of Sheila and her mother. Mrs. Watkins was in the intensive care unit with no rational hope of recovery. As the weeks dragged on, Sheila was torn between the desire to have her mother's suffering over and the profound sense of loss that she would feel when her mother was unambiguously gone. Each part of the dilemma was a legitimate expression of her love for her mother.

She had watched her mother withstand one terrible complication after another. With each complication her mother became inexorably weaker. Mrs. Watkins had more tubes, lines and catheters than anyone else in that ICU. Sheila was never sure what, if anything, might be going on in her mother's mind because there was no way she could have communicated through that mass of wires. There could be no doubt that her mother was not going to survive this experience and leave the ICU, much less the hospital, or return home in any state.

Sheila did not wish to have her mother subjected to any more poking needles or tubes. Nevertheless, with equal fervor, Sheila did not want her mother to die. As long as her mother was even a little bit alive she could fantasize that some miracle would restore her. She could go to the ICU and hold her mother's hand and remember all the wonderful times of her childhood when they had been so close. How alone she felt when she thought of her mother as already gone. There was no basis on which to reconcile these conflicting considerations.

What made this situation even worse was that while appreciating each part of the dilemma and recognizing the impossibility of reconciling them, Sheila thought that this was a sign of madness, that she was going crazy. She thought all problems had to have a solution. She had never thought about the nature of ambivalence and how it might relate to her life.

She had never thought that perfectly normal, sane people could find a situation in which a solution was so impossible.

The simple problems of life generally do have solutions. We may not like the solutions and wish they were otherwise, but we can generally agree about their validity. It is only when we get to the complex issues that reach deep into our hearts and souls that we uncover the anguish of ambivalence. Obviously, Sheila's growing appreciation of the ambivalence she felt was not a sign of mental illness but rather of emotional growth. And the catalyst for this emotional growth was her immersion into the life and death issues of medical crisis.

Appropriate Independence and Unhealthy Codependence

When we are born, we are totally dependent upon others, mostly our parents. Our childhood and adolescence are consumed by the journey to independence. Not everyone makes it. Some have intellectual failings. Others, at a critical juncture, may lack support and be left stranded in emotional adolescence.

Do not worry that our development is too fragile a thread. The human psyche, just as the human body, has a resilience from redundant compensating systems. If we fail on one path we can go on to another. Parents get tired and cranky. They may worry about next month's rent or how secure their job may be or what the mammogram may tell about the new lump in their sister's breast.

If the emotional development of children depended on being exposed only to the "right" answer every time, no one would ever achieve healthy independence.

Children respond to communication patterns. You have more than one chance to make it come out alright. On the other hand, life is not an exam in which you can parrot the right answer once and then promptly forget it. The questions come up over and over again, and consistency is important.

The sins of the fathers are visited upon the children. If you grew up in a family that had a hard time giving children appropriate independence, you are going to do what you know when your turn as a parent comes. As time passes and generations change, so do the ideas of what may be appropriate independence. The length of hair, formalities of address and dinner table conversation, much less whether dinner takes place at a table, all have significance beyond their superficial appearance. These are some of the struggles that contribute to the tensions of the normal parent-child relationship.

This relationship survives childhood. Parents may continue to behave as if the authority of their suggestions had the same significance when the child is 28 as it did when the child was 8. Similarly, children may react to a request with an outburst more appropriate to an 8-year-old rather than appreciating the spirit in which the request was made. This struggle goes on in the most innocuous of circumstances.

Between Living Pain and Painless Death

Several books have been published in recent years exploring the pitfalls and emotional booby traps of such role reversal in times of illness. None is better than Philip Roth's *Patrimony*. Herman Roth was the archetypical independent man. He did things his way, depending only on his own interpretation of the moral code to which he subscribed and of which he was principal author. Not surprisingly, growing up in a family with such a patriarch was not easy. The conflict between a father's certainty and an adolescent's drive for independence produces frequent emotional fireworks.

In this book, the struggle continues into maturity. Then as his father develops an inoperable brain tumor, the roles gradually shift. As his father slowly declines, Roth has to lead, but not always and not in everything. And sometimes he finds that his father is still just a little ahead of him, as when Roth starts to speak of living wills and finds his father agreeing with arguments not yet completed.

At the end, despite having discussed and agreed about the futility of continuing medical treatment beyond the chance of meaningful life, Philip Roth finds himself staring into the abyss. His father is unconscious in the emergency room. He has been unconscious for twelve hours. There is no question that he cannot be resuscitated; even his insensible life is ebbing fast. The emergency room doctor asks Philip whether he wants a tube inserted in his father's windpipe to help him breathe. This is against his father's expressed wishes and Philip neither wants this useless intervention done to himself nor to his father.

Nevertheless when the moment comes, he needs more time. "How could I take it on myself to decide that my father should be finished with life . . . ?" He eventually honors his father's request but not without the pain and terrible sense of loss of the living. His poignant description of this visceral struggle stands forever as a tribute to his father.

The loss that Andrew Malcolm suffers in *Someday* takes longer. The decline of his mother, both intellectually and physically, years before her death, produces a different pain. Bea Malcolm slips into a manipulative, passive mode and allows the world to contract around her. The dominant tone of Malcolm's book is his inability to come to terms with his mother's decline. He tries to draw her into his family—his wife and children—but she resists. He tries to enlarge the dimensions of her world, but she refuses. Yet, she is alive and can relate to him in her own idiosyncratic way. There is still a connection.

Bea Malcolm's physical decline finally results in her having a tube placed in her windpipe, and Andrew Malcolm has to suffer the agony of asking for it to be removed. He loses his mother twice—first her soul, then her body. This double loss is accentuated in those families in which the parent suffers from Alzheimer's disease or some other progressive mental defect. To watch the physical decline of a parent is painful, but the alteration in appearance is a constant reminder of the underlying change that is taking place. When the change is mental without physical alteration, the recurring shock of seeing the shell without the substance is haunting.

Between Love and Hate

These situations illustrate ambivalence. The child remembers the parent, and those memories are linked to the flesh and bones of the parent. The child dreads terribly the parent's suffering as he dreads the waning of his memories. He fears the loss of his childhood and he fears his own mortality. While the parent lives, however insensible, the memories have a greater intensity. The cost of that perceived intensity is the pain of the parent's suffering. The corporality of the parent versus the relief of pain of the parent is the dilemma that galvanizes this ambivalence.

The ambivalence experienced in most family relationships evolves from the complexity of love. The loss of the loved parent as opposed to the suffering of the loved parent.

This is not the only kind of ambivalence. There is another ambivalence that occurs more often then we acknowledge—as a result of serious deficiency or violation of the parent-child relation-ship. We are not talking about the frustration and guilt one feels for having been reprimanded after failing to perform or follow through some parentally expected task.

A tragic situation is one in which the ambivalence is between love and hate of the parent—where the loss of a parent may be grieved but also celebrated as the deliverance of just desserts.

We are concerned about the situation of real neglect or abuse of a child. Alcoholism, substance abuse and mental illness are unfortu-nate realities of modern life. These problems do not preclude parent-ing although they may well preclude effective parenting. The result is millions of children growing up in families in which a parent is so impaired by personal problems that he or she cannot provide a con-sistent positive emotional environment. Worse still are those situations in which the child has been abused verbally, physically or sexually.

Many experienced clergymen, psychologists and psychiatrists have addressed themselves to the problems of people who have suf-fered such a grievous harm. Many books and tapes have been pro-duced to guide such wounded persons in coming to grips with these offenses and to learn to grow emotionally beyond them.

Nothing I write can be a substitute for the hard but valuable work these others have proposed. My concern, however, is helping the family when such a parent may be seriously ill. The decisions you make and the actions you take may have irretrievable consequences.

If you can keep this medical part of your relationship on a sound basis, it may provide a foundation for dealing with other issues. At least, you will not suffer the unnecessary results of irre-versible acts if the parent dies.

The dilemma of ambivalence may continue,
because you have appropriate reasons for it.
Understanding the appropriateness of that ambivalence may,
indeed, be the first step toward dealing with it effectively.

To try to ignore or deny the ambivalence leads to greater internal confusion on your part and an inconsistent approach in dealing with your parent which is quite counterproductive. There are some very useful principles which can be extracted from the experience of others who have been there before. Two books in particular have given exceptional insight into the emotional struggles of children with this plight. Louie Anderson has written *Dear Dad: Letters from an Adult Child* about his relationship with an alcoholic father. Sylvia Fisher has written a very moving account of the incest she suffered by her father in *My Father's House.*

Coming to Grips

There are four steps in dealing with such circumstances as you adjust your thinking and acting to here and now:

1. Take charge of the relationship today.
2. Give yourself some distance.
3. Understand the cause of your parent's emotional failure.
4. Forgive your parent.

This prescription may seem like an impossibly difficult order, given the harm you have suffered. As you will see there is a balance to this outline and a validity derived from the experience of others. If your parent is ill, there may be a pressing urgency to begin this process while you still have the opportunity to resolve these issues. It is always easier to do this while your parent is still alive.

Take charge of the relationship today. What do we mean by taking charge? I have specifically not said, "Take responsibility." Most children in this situation have already assigned too much responsibility to themselves—responsibility for the behavior of others toward them. They have been led to believe that they are responsible for the abuse to which they have been subjected. They think that they are in some way responsible for the alcoholism of the parent—that if they had been more obedient, more successful, more attractive, their parent would not have been moved to alcoholism.

So many act as if their parent's alcoholism is punishment for some inadequacy of their own.

Obviously, a child is not responsible for a parent's sickness—whatever its nature. A child can only be responsible for himself and for his own behavior. Now is the time for the child to take charge, to no longer be exploited by undeserved guilt. The limits of acceptable expectations need to be established. The parent has to be informed of what help can be expected and what requests will not be respected. Control will have shifted from parent to child, but this time without the presumption of manipulation.

Give yourself some distance. After a lifetime of undeserved guilt, the expectation that the psychological framework of the family relationship will change overnight is truly unrealistic. Such change involves a lot of hard work and pain and will not succeed if the interaction between parent and child is too constant. The pressures of the old patterns are too great. You need to provide yourself some distance: to give you a chance to stay to your plan, to get a breather from the emotional intensity of the involvement, to regroup.

Distance means different things to different people. To some it may be across the street, to others across the country. Distance may mean just having a telephone answering machine or an unlisted telephone number, or finding someone else to supervise a parent's care. You need to be candid with yourself about the distance you require. If things are not working out, you may need to seek greater distance. You cannot help your parent unless you can create an emotional safe harbor for yourself. Distance is a key ingredient in creating that safe harbor.

Understand the cause of your parent's emotional failure. If you can withdraw from the field of battle, from the hurt and conflict, you may be able to analyze how your parent got there. By your taking charge, your parent is no longer bigger than life. By giving yourself distance, you should be able to get a perspective on the factors in your parent's life. Being an abusing parent is not fun. No one grows up waiting for the moment he can inflict pain on his children. Abused children grow up promising never to do to another what they have suffered, and then they go ahead and do it. Why? Because they do not know any better.

Almost all abusive parents have been the victims of abuse themselves. It is all they have ever seen or learned or know. It is the example than was literally knocked into their heads.

Abusive parents can often be very kind. The child thinks the parent is being kind because of something the child has done or not done. The child begins to believe that his behavior is the determinant of the parent's behavior. This is the terrible result of the mercurial inconsistency of a parent's behavior.

The fact is that the parent's behavior is determined by how the parent feels. If the parent feels safe and not threatened by outside forces or his own demons, he may be able to relate appropriately to the child for awhile. But then in the blink of an eye, the situation can change. The shouts, the sarcasm, the blows begin again. Children have a great capacity for magical thinking and these rapid changes stimulate it even more. The sick parent does not understand his own psychological dynamics and will probably blame the child, reinforcing the child's mistaken belief.

Once this sick dance begins it can go on for years, until the child is able to stand back and see what is really happening. Again, learning more about the parent's childhood, the forces that produced this tortured and uncontrolled monster, will strengthen the perspective that distance has begun.

Forgive your parent. Abusive parents who become seriously ill do not all react the same way. For some, there may be a regression to more overtly childlike relations and a willingness to be cared for in a way they never were before. This may be an awful turnabout because that parent wants something that he never gave to you. One normal reaction is to take the opportunity to psychologically kick him in the teeth. Don't do it! You may be the most deserving person to get your licks, but don't do it. Not because you owe something to your parent, not because he or she deserves better, but because it will make things harder for you. It will prevent you from accomplishing the work that you need to do.

A Time to Question

The overtly needy parent will be more pliant, more willing to talk to you about childhood memories. This is an important beginning. Your anger and negative feelings may be so great that you couldn't possibly talk about something important to you. However, your parent's childhood will naturally be interesting to you. He can describe people whom you have only known as old when they were young. Events and unfamiliar activities can become real.

Don't feel that you have to psychoanalyze your parent, you probably won't be able to anyway. Just listen. You may see some parallels between your parent's life and yours.

Your father or mother may have the most important memories buried so deep that it may take a long time to get to them. For the moment just keep the conversation going.

You can ask:

What were things like when you were young?
What was your father like?
What was your first job?
Who was your best friend?
What was your favorite trip with your parents?
What was the saddest thing that happened to you as a child?

A Complicated Journey With an Uncertain Outcome

This is not a discussion that is going to be completed in an hour—or a day. Look at it as a serious job that is necessary for your survival, because it is. You are looking for the word, the phrase, the image which will trigger that next step in your journey: forgiving your parent for the terrible things he has done to you.

A still angry and demanding parent will be more difficult to work with than a pliant parent. He is more likely to try to maintain the upper hand and manipulate you. He may try to blame his current sickness on the stress you or someone else may have given him years ago. Don't argue; he won't be listening. The louder you reply the more sure he will be that he is right. Softly agree that he has had a hard life, and ask how he would have liked to have done things differently. This may get him into a discussion of how things were. It can provide you an opening to get the information you need.

These discussions are not easy. Your parent cannot deal with stress well to begin with. If he could, you would not have been subjected to the violence of his frustration. Now he is in a situation that is stressful. Serious illness means a complicated journey and an uncertain outcome. He may have many specific and realistic fears. As you have been a familiar whipping boy in the past, he may fall into his usual behavior patterns.

Don't let him. If he starts to shout and call you names, do not shout in reply. Quietly, say that you are both adults and you do not think this is an appropriate way for adults to talk. If he keeps it up or starts to become physically abusive, pick yourself up and leave. As you leave, always keep open the option of returning by saying that you want to come back again when he is feeling more like himself.

These discussions are not debates. The point is not to convince your parent that he has been bad and you have been abused. It is unlikely that you will ever achieve that goal.

Your true goal is for you to see what happened and why.

Not that you need more repetition of what you have suffered. But you do need to learn what happened to your parent, and you need to understand why he may have behaved as he did. These discussions are a time for you to question. You have to direct the discussion and try to maintain the emotional environment so that you get the answers. If he gets your goat and it ends up in a shouting match, you will never succeed in this vital enterprise.

Stay calm on the outside, no matter how you may be seething below the surface. When it gets to be too much, leave. Treasure your distance. But distance alone will not give you the answers. Understanding requires communication. However, distance may give you the quiet necessary to pursue that communication and the pause to reflect on the information.

Understanding means that both you and your parent see that you both are victims. In many psychological circles these days it is bad form to refer to the individual as a "victim." The word victim carries the notion of lack of power, and all efforts are designed to bring you back to power.

I do not agree with the avoidance of the word victim. There are many forces over which we do not have power. The sun will rise tomorrow morning no matter what I think. Federal taxes are due in April and I had better have the money. That both my mother and father were short precluded me from having the height to be a professional basketball player.

There are many areas in which we are powerless and we had better concentrate on pursuing our true options rather than believe we have *all* options.

It is better to determine what we *can* alter and control, and seek to do this as effectively as possible. As we have discussed, you are in control of your reaction to the abuse you may have suffered. You are not in control of your parent's reaction, and if you make the alteration of your parent's reaction a prime goal, you are very likely to fail.

A more reasonable goal is to understand the way in which your parent was a victim of the forces of his childhood. This may be very difficult to investigate. Your parent may have suppressed the details of the abuse he suffered, or it may have occurred at a time which is effectively before memory. While these represent serious obstacles, they do not make the task impossible. Abuse does not occur on only one occasion. It happens over and over again. Year in and year out. It represents a pattern of behavior which is reiterated in many ways. The important distortion may have occurred before memory, and the most flagrant examples may be deeply hidden by protective psychological mechanisms, but the fingerprints are there if you will look for them.

Your Ambivalence Toward Forgiveness

To recognize your parent as a victim takes the responsibility away from you. You were not the cause of your parent's drinking. Your behavior was not the reason you were thrown down the stairs and broke your arm. It was not your seduction which precipitated a sexual assault. All these terrible parental reactions were conditioned by equally terrible experiences in that parent's childhood which were unrecognized and for which he never received any explanation or help.

When the outside stresses in this parent's life got to be too much, he behaved in the only way that he had been taught and in the way he had probably sworn he never would. He abused you. And he knows it down deep in his hidden heart. And that knowledge shares the same terrible place with the memories of what he suffered when he was a child. In a different context, Philip Roth said, ". . . what goes into survival isn't always pretty." It is the perversion of this drive for survival which fuels the abuse. The cycle of victimization will continue until you take charge and stop it.

The process of gathering information, analyzing and understanding it is important, because without it there will be no true forgiveness. And forgiveness is the destination of this journey.

The importance of forgiveness is not for your parent. It is for you. Without forgiveness, you cannot get on with the rest of your life. Without forgiveness, you will rehearse and relive all the horrors you have suffered over and over again. Without forgiveness, you will not be able to reconcile the ambivalence that can play such a large role in dealing with serious illness.

Until you reach the point of understanding, forgiveness seems absurd or worse—some unthinkable pious exhortation that denies your own suffering. With understanding, forgiveness becomes compelling because it is the critical feature in stopping the cycle of abuse. Writing to his dead alcoholic father in *Dear Dad*, Louie Anderson says, "Dad, the way I see it, you died without ever confronting your innermost fears, and I'm not going to allow myself to follow the same route."

And Sylvia Fraser in *My Father's House* writes, ". . . my father was not a monster. His life was a bud that never opened, blighted by the first frost. His crime became his prison, his guilt, his bars . . . Though I don't understand him, I can pity him and forgive him. I forgive my father so I can forgive myself . . . Mine turns out to be a story without villains. Children who were in some way abused, abuse others; victims become villains. Thus, not to forgive only perpetuates the crime, creates more victims . . ."

In writing this book, I have spent a lot of time thinking about the issues of the abused child confronting the critical illness of the parent and what kind of a response would bring the most lasting resolution. During the course of this intellectual rumination, one of my oldest friends, and a man whose physician I was, developed a fatal brain tumor. He was the most loyal of friends and a brilliant man whose accomplishments in life were thwarted by the psychological results of a childhood of mental abuse.

Over the course of our 30-year friendship, I often wondered what he might have accomplished without this burden. What made it worse was that he had had two abusive parents and throughout his life had overtly idolized one of them. He appeared oblivious to the degree to which this parent had participated in and continued to perpetuate the abuse which had begun in infancy. His inability to confront this required him to keep deeply hidden from himself the innermost reaches of his being. Unfortunately, he had chosen to become a writer, but his failure to communicate honestly with himself crippled his ability to reach the soul of his audience.

During the course of his illness, he spent time wondering about his feelings for his parents, one of whom was still alive, the other having died a few years before. He finally began to recognize the extent to which he had maintained the fiction of the "good parent." He had no regrets about his actions when that parent died. He had been a model son. He had cared for that parent and maintained a hospital vigil in the most devoted manner. Afterward he had arranged for a funeral which all of us attended as an act of respect for our friend.

Recognizing that his "good parent" had not been good at all, he began to think about the other, to whom he had previously attributed all his trouble. He began to remember her terrible bouts of hallucinations and depression, the tides of mental illness which tortured her as they had confused and tortured my friend. Yes, the bizarre punishments and erratic alternation of praise and derision took place as remembered. The pain as a child and the memory of the pain as an adult were no less because of this information.

They were horrible and disabling experiences and they could not be undone. His life had been irreparably damaged. But what was he to do? Although he was ill, my friend was always hopeful that he could still work. He had to get on with his life, and the understanding that there was a cause for his torture other than his own "badness" made this possible.

My friend realized, before I did, that the only way to come to peace with the "demon" of his childhood was forgiveness.

Unfortunately, as he was beginning this process, he had a fatal seizure and died. Nevertheless he died with an affirmative mental attitude. He had finally taken charge and forgiveness was the proof of his new power.

My friend's story has several lessons, with which I will finish this chapter:

♦ **It is never too late to make your life better.** Although we don't know what may be in store for us, slaying the demons of our childhood will make us more capable.

✦ **The work we do in our parents' illnesses is repaid by a feeling of accomplishment.** This allows us to move on to the next stage in our own lives. The work we do not only satisfies a debt that we feel from even the most adverse childhood, but frees us to expand our horizons.

✦ **No matter how horribly you have been abused and how deeply you believe the hate has been burned into you, you are really ambivalent.** The instinctual need for parental approval becomes an even more powerful demon as you deny it. By offering forgiveness, you empower yourself as no other act can.

✦ **You can start forgiving right now.** You don't know how long the opportunity may remain. In my friend's case, his life was running out faster than anyone could know. In yours, it may be that of one of your parents. Reconciling with a living parent offers an enormous feeling of accomplishment.

Louie Anderson sums up all we have learned when he writes:

"I forgive you. I understand. I realize why I have come here and what I have been looking for all this time. I wanted to be with you. And now I am and always will be. Oh, yeah. There's one more thing that I haven't said but want to. And that one thing is, I love you."

CHAPTER NINE

Fear and the Laws of Nature

The experience of serious illness is filled with many fears—some very immediate; others more remote. Ironically, the more concrete and immediate the fear, the easier it is to confront. Vague fears are too easily magnified by the imagination. The crux of bravery may well be to pull fear from behind our magnifying glass. By examining it carefully, the brave person manages fear and prevents its rampant expansion. The bright light of scrutiny clarifies the monstrosity as the shadows of our own imagination.

The Fear Factor

The emotional strain of a serious diagnosis may result in a failure of judgment on the part of a patient. We hope that the fear of abandonment will have been at least partially relieved by your presence and interest, but there are other fears. Many of them are realistic and well founded but the degree to which they are emphasized may be inappropriate.

Do not dismiss these fears as silly. They are very real and sometimes more threatening than death to certain sufferers. Try to find out the limits of the phobia and what modifying circumstances might reduce the fear:

✦ Will the presence of another, specific person lessen the fear?
✦ Are there types of sedation or pain relievers in the past that have helped?

✦ Are there alternative ways of accomplishing the same end without the specific phobia-inducing procedure?

The patient, ashamed of the phobia, may not wish to reveal it and may claim to make a decision on another basis.

If a decision seems strange, I always try to lead the patient through his reasoning process to see if I can detect a hidden fear that may be distorting a decision. Sometimes I can determine it, but many times I may not until later.

Sam's Phobia

Sam was getting increasingly severe cramps in his right leg after walking only a dozen yards. He was sure that it was due to poor circulation and knew his cigarette smoking played a significant part in aggravating it. He had not been to see a doctor for several years because they all said the same thing: Stop smoking, stop eating the foods you love and take a lot of medicines. What kind of a man would he be if he submitted to that kind of advice?

Sam had always been able to take care of himself. He left high school before graduating to take care of his family after his father had died of lung cancer. He had developed a food supply business in the Bronx. He would go down to the wholesale markets at four a.m. to get the best buys of the day in vegetables and fruits, then sell them to local markets and restaurants in his neighborhood. It was physically hard work, lifting the crates up and off the back of the truck. It was also dangerous.

He dealt in cash and always carried a couple of thousand dollars with him. He had to buy the supplies, then receive the money when he sold them. There were plenty of people in the places he worked who were prepared to take his money by force. Several who had tried suffered broken limbs from the weighted baseball bat he kept in the truck cab. Besides, Sam was a pretty big fellow. If he saw you coming, his look was very dissuading.

Doris, his wife, was always trying to get him to stop smoking. She had watched her father die of emphysema and did not want to see that happen to her husband. When Sam kept getting a severe cramp in his right calf, Doris forced him to see the doctor.

The doctor said it was not due to an old knee injury but to a reduction of blood flow in the main artery going to his leg. The first step would be to stop smoking.

Depending upon his physical response, the next step would be to do an angiogram to examine the anatomy of the blood vessel. This was a common procedure with an excellent success rate but there were occasional complications. The catheter might cause a clot or pierce the blood vessel. Very rarely would amputation result. But the first step was to stop smoking and keep walking to try to stimulate blood flow.

Sam stopped smoking for two days. After that he gave up and hired a young kid from the neighborhood to ride the truck with him to do a lot of the running. That worked for a couple of years. If anyone saw him limping, he claimed it was the effect of the morning dampness on his old knee injury. He stayed away from doctors. His wife finally gave up nagging him. He fumed anytime she mentioned it.

The ostrich approach would not work forever. A crate of avocados fell off the back of the truck onto Sam's foot. It hurt a lot but in the cold of the morning it was soon forgotten. Sam barely remembered the injury when he took his shoes off early that afternoon and saw the bloody mess from which he peeled away his sock. He washed the area carefully with soap and water and wondered if he should put on one of those antibiotic salves advertised on television. He didn't tell his wife. She would have started up again about going to see Dr. Ramsey.

The next morning he was glad he could get his foot back into the shoe without too much pain. He felt more throbbing as the morning wore on and began to feel flushed. The market air was frigid. Even the woolen cap and double jackets were poor insulation. Because the flushing made him dizzy, he went home early.

When he took his shoe off, his toe looked disgusting. It had turned many colors, none of them healthy, and there was a trickle of thin pus from the main wound. Sam washed the toe again with soap and water and tried to keep his foot up to relieve the growing pain. This time Doris saw the blood stain on the white sock. She gasped when she removed the sock and saw his toe. "Sam, you've got to see the doctor right away. That toe is infected. You need an antibiotic."

"Oh, it's just bruised a bit," he said. "It was worse yesterday. It'll be better tomorrow."

But it was not better. The throbbing was worse and there were some black spots around the wound. Not even Sam thought he could get on the truck that morning. He agreed to go to the doctor with Doris.

Dr. Ramsey looked at the wound shaking his head sadly. "Why didn't you come back sooner, Sam? I asked you to see what you could do by stopping smoking, but I told you there were many other things that we could do to improve your circulation. This infection looks pretty bad. We stand some chance of healing it but there's a chance of losing the toe or even more."

"Well, Doc, the way I look at it I've gained two years. When we talked before you said you wanted to do some test that could make me lose the leg. If I lose it now, I'll have had it two years longer than if I let you at it."

Dr. Ramsey sat quietly on the stool above the festering toe. He remembered the afternoon he talked with Sam about his circulation and he remembered the off-handed way in which he mentioned the possible but very rare complications of the angiogram. He had not meant to suggest that the test was hazardous but just that it was a serious undertaking. If stopping smoking worked then it would not be necessary to take any risks.

The doctor had meant to *encourage* Sam in his attempt to stop smoking—not to frighten him away from treatment.

Sam was a man whose livelihood and indeed his life depended upon his physical abilities. A one-legged trucker would not last very long in the vegetable market. Sam had put away money for his retirement but he had not planned on its necessity quite yet. Besides his youngest son still had two years of college left and was talking about going to law school. Who was going to pay for that?

Sam had seen his father lose his job when lung cancer prevented him from shoveling coal any longer. When he lost his job, the family had to depend on the church and neighbors for almost everything. When he died Sam left school to help. He felt shame for his family's predicament and sadness for his own loss of opportunity. He was sure that wouldn't ever happen to his family. The threat of any loss of his physical abilities frightened him as little else would.

When he heard Dr. Ramsey say that he could lose his leg, Sam could hear nothing else. The loss of his leg was worse than the loss of his life. If he died, his family would get some insurance; if he lived without a leg, he would have to watch his family suffer. Better to die. Dr. Ramsey could not say anything that would scare him more. And Sam's fear was so great, he could not even bring it up to the doctor.

Sam's failure to follow a rational treatment plan depended on unspoken, indeed hidden, fears and values of which Dr. Ramsey was ignorant. Despite his concern for Sam, the doctor fell into the unseen trap. Unwittingly, he said the thing that would most thoroughly interfere with his ability to help his patient. Dr. Ramsey is not alone. Doctors misunderstand their patients; and families, their loved ones. All of us have done this and will continue to do this. Not because we don't care or because we don't spend enough time trying to elicit information, but because the patient may try to hide the fears from himself as well as from others. We have to recognize the inevitability of our inadequacies and be vigilant for behavior that doesn't seem to make sense.

This is as important for the family as for the doctor. It may give us an opportunity to head off an ill-fated undertaking before it is too far along. The same difficulty that Dr. Ramsey had understanding Sam's fears can be found in families everywhere.

Family members have the advantage of having spent more time with the patient. They know more about secret fears that may be behind decisions. They can help by alerting the doctor.

Even if they don't understand the reasons behind a decision, they may see that the patient is not focusing clearly on the important issues that face him. They can alert the doctor about this too. The family has the advantage of just sitting and listening to the patient talk about his fears. The patient is less likely to be intimidated by family than the doctor.

But a doctor will have to listen to the patient. A doctor cannot allow his or her own fears for the patient to disrupt communication. A doctor must listen, not try to dominate the conversation, and ask a patient what he fears most. If the patient can't be specific, the doctor can be. The doctor can ask the patient if it's pain, death, working, not working, cost or whatever. Sometimes just getting a patient to talk may help him understand worries that he didn't know he had.

Understanding your worries will make them easier to deal with and help the patient settle on a course of action that reflects his real needs. That is what communication is all about.

Breaking Down Our Fears

Like the other problems we have discussed, dealing with fear is more successfully mastered by breaking it into its components. Then we can overcome terror one piece at a time:

+ First, we have to identify the fear. What exactly am I afraid of?

+ Next, isolate the fear from its emotional context. Why does this possibility create such a terrible reaction in me?

+ What is the absolutely worst thing that could happen to us?

+ What preparation will minimize this possibility?

+ If it should occur anyway, what can be done to soften its impact?

As we shall see, these steps can put the cosmic terror on a human scale. Concentrating on these mental steps puts you in control of your life and helps you banish anxiety.

As President Franklin Roosevelt said in the dark days of the Great Depression, ". . . the only thing we have to fear is fear itself."

The Different Kinds of Fear

What specific fears do we find? There are many.

Medical costs. Medical care can be very expensive. The uninsured patient with a serious illness represents a national tragedy for which a solution must be found. However, many patients who are quite well insured and have more than adequate financial resources may focus on the cost of alternative treatments rather than other aspects of appropriateness.

Treatment. In other instances the patient may have an inordinate fear of a certain kind of treatment and this phobia will distort his choice. Examples of this include fears of pain, anesthesia or closed spaces as in special radiology exams such as an MRI.

Pain. An aching tooth, a gallbladder attack, and a fractured vertebra represent a wide spectrum. How one bears pain will often depend on the importance of the condition. Most of these conditions have no greater psychological meaning than the level of discomfort they represent. The pain of a heart attack or an incisional pain after a cancer operation will have very different meaning.

For the most part, pain is a concrete fear and the relief of it is a straightforward problem. Difficulties arise when the physician does not recognize the intensity of the pain and fails to prescribe adequate doses of analgesics or narcotics; or the nurse, when given discretion, fails to administer appropriate doses at proper intervals.

These are human failings of experience or understanding. The doctor and nurse may believe that they are protecting the patient from drug addiction. How silly! If the emotional concerns of the patient are met by the staff and anxiety appropriately treated by other medicines, the demand for narcotics decreases to that required for the bare pain.

As the incision heals or the bone regrows, the need for pain relief declines but the need for emotional support does not.

Morphine is not an adequate substitute for sitting down and alleviating a patient's worries about the future. This use of morphine is useless, inappropriate and addicting. It represents a professional failure.

Confrontation with mortality. Some part of the fear of pain is really fear of death. The patient worries about the uncertainty of the outcome. The realization that some people with these illnesses die, changes the perception of pain. With every twinge the patient worries that the disease has not been contained, that the cancer is spreading to new areas or that the area of dying heart muscle is enlarging. Anxiety and fear increase the intensity of pain, recruiting many new nerve fibers. Preparation and control can reduce this, short-circuiting the nerve impulses before they reach the brain.

There are some people who are truly phobic about death. The conventional culture of the United States is to be positive, optimistic, which makes death unmentionable. Death is no longer a natural and inevitable conclusion of life but a failure of the "fix-it" industry. The patient's heart did not wear out from use; it wasn't treated quickly enough or cleverly enough. Or it did not respond to the applied measures with the expected salutary response.

In many cases, there is a psychological need to affix blame on someone or something or some institution. A corollary of this has been that often this affixing of blame has a legal element which can result in considerable financial damages. Not only do family members have an opportunity to reject the concept of death, including their own deaths, as natural but they can be well paid for this escapism at the same time. In this cultural context it becomes difficult to discern death-phobia and differentiate it from other categories of fear. A phobia—whether death-phobia, claustrophobia or acrophobia—is the irrational fear of some thing or condition which is not amenable to remedy by any intellectual or emotional discourse or physical demonstration. As such, it requires treatment in a professional environment and not by a book.

Our view of death is conditioned by religious belief. If you have a well formed view of heaven and hell and believe that each of us will answer for our behavior at a time of judgment in an afterlife, your expectations will be different from the person who believes that our brief visit on this planet is all there is, and once it ends we have neither spiritual nor physical persistence. While religious beliefs most commonly remain a source of comfort from the troubles of everyday life, they need not always. An apprehensive person may fear the judgment of God far more than any pain he is likely to suffer on earth and want, therefore, to avoid death at any cost. By contrast, a narcissistic scoundrel may welcome death as an easy escape when his wickedness has run its course.

**The sense of eternity that imbues most religious thought
can be calming to a family worried about the outcome
of serious illness.**

The family will take comfort in the thought that the soul persists whatever the uncertainty of the outcome. Although most religious thought attempts to cultivate our concern for others, its appeal to our sense of personal permanence may be its most important feature for some people.

A curious variation of this is represented by my friend, Roger, who had been truly phobic about death since college. He was always horrified to hear about anyone's death. He anxiously read anything that purported to teach him how to live longer. He exercised compulsively. He followed his blood pressure and cholesterol levels as some men follow the stock market. Since I was Roger's physician as well as his friend from college, he consulted me often both in the office and anywhere else about the value of the newest health claim. I spent years deflecting his incessant questions but I never thought about the real worry behind them.

Roger's incessant questioning was directed not only at his friends but at himself as well. He had not grown up in any particular religious tradition and had no real sense of a hereafter. He was unsure about the nature of the world but he did not feel that his personality would survive his death in any form. His fear of death was an expression of his fear that when he died he would disappear without a trace. He was not rich in money and not particularly successful professionally. These accomplishments would never ensure the immortality which he sought so earnestly. His recognition of this reality drove him even more strenuously. His search for this immortality curiously led him to a congregation in which he could maintain his honest agnosticism. His relief resulted from his conviction that this congregation would be immortal. As a member, his name would forever be inscribed on its rolls.

Roger's devotion to this congregation was total. He proselytized among his friends and even among those he knew less well.

What was at first a social annoyance became less objectionable when the reason for his emotional investment was understood. He was able to satisfy his need for immortality by transferring it from himself to an institution. His practical experience forced him to recognize that he would not live forever in his present form. He was not able to conceive any honest belief in a hereafter and yet he was able to satisfy his emotional needs by focusing on the expected unlimited life of his adopted congregation. Roger found a unique solution to a formidable problem.

Fear for your family. This concern is often paramount. How will they survive without you? Who will pay for the groceries? Or answer your children's questions about right and wrong and God and going to church? Who will guide them when they are confused and need direction? These kinds of questions change as your family changes. Leaving an infant invokes different fears than leaving an 18-year-old.

Grown children with families of their own generally do not demand a concern for material support or the intensity of guidance that younger children do. You may worry about how your spouse will fare without you. Sometimes this may have an economic basis but often it results from a growing closer together as infirmities may create a greater interdependence. Who will make sure your husband takes his heart pills? Who will clear the snow off the stoop in winter so that your wife won't fall? No one will have quite the personal caring or knowledge to do these things as well as you.

Fear of abandonment. There are alternative responses to this situation. Perhaps the couple has grown apart. The petty disagreements have festered into barely concealed hostilities. The fear of illness may result in a fear of being abandoned in a time of need. Perhaps the drive for longevity is the wish to be the one left in peace after the other has died. Maybe the prize is to be the one left behind and dying means you have lost the contest. People and relationships among people take many different forms. I have learned never to assume that things are as they seem. The most contentious spouses can have the strongest ties to each other. And the superficial affection of others may disguise the empty shell of a withered relationship.

HORACE AND LILLIAN

Horace and Lillian raised their family in discord. Dinner time was often the acme of emotional conflict. Shouts and rattling dishes accompanied every meal. Horace was a pretty good electrician and came home at 6:30 every night complaining about the problems he faced that day. Lillian spent the day trying to balance the family budget and save a little for the rainy day that her parents had forgotten about. Her parents lived in the apartment at the back of their small house until their hearts gave out within six months of each other. Horace couldn't stand them and did not see why Lillian should spend so much time looking after them and spending his hard earned money to support them. Why hadn't they bothered to worry about their own future?

Horace and Lillian's children frequently wondered why their parents had stayed together so long. Tears, recriminations, slamming doors punctuated the days of their youth. They had failed to see that the only things that Horace and Lillian agreed about were the issues of child-rearing. No child could engineer a serious split in their united front. The children took for granted their parents' interest in finished homework and prompt arrival home. It wasn't necessarily fun but they knew what the rules were and the penalty for not following them.

After the last child graduated from high school, Lillian and Horace argued even more, and now there was no longer the mutual project to bring them back after the explosion. Finally, Lillian told Horace to leave until he behaved in a more civil fashion. She did not need him any longer. She could go off and find a job to support herself. When she took a job as a receptionist for a local lawyer, Horace moved in with one of his sons who traveled and wasn't home much.

I had been seeing Horace for increasing back pain.

The mental stress of his home life had contributed as much to his malady as an injury he sustained when he fell off a ladder while wiring his own house. The pain got much worse after he started sleeping on his son's couch. He tried some exercise, physical therapy and various muscle relaxants. The pain kept getting worse and eventually he had to stop working.

I put him in the hospital for traction and big league sedation. He finally slept but the pain did not diminish. Despite maximum efforts Horace got little relief and surgery was scheduled. This was some years ago when back surgery was far more extensive than the kind done today. I didn't worry much about Horace's ability to withstand or benefit from the surgery but I had serious worries about his recovery if he returned to his son's couch.

Lillian was not my patient. I am not sure she saw anyone regularly, probably not even her gynecologist. Nevertheless, I knew her by sight and thought I had seen her leaving the hospital one day as I was arriving. I asked Horace about it and he said she had begun visiting him when he was laid up at his son's and couldn't cook for himself. Her cooking hadn't improved any but he was grateful not to starve and she seemed easier to get along with. They talked about the children and their struggles getting them raised, funny little incidents that had woven their lives so tightly together. When I put Horace in the hospital, Lillian continued to visit although she no longer felt obliged to cook.

I couldn't really schedule Horace's surgery until I had an idea of where he would recover. It wasn't fair to wait until the last moment when we would discharge him. I asked him if he thought Lillian would be willing to let him go back to their house just to recover from the surgery. He broke out in a big smile and said he didn't know but he would sure be grateful if I would ask her for him. His smile encouraged me to try to play Cupid. When I asked Lillian, she smiled too and said the house was just too big for her alone and since Horace owned half of it anyway she would be willing to have him recuperate there.

Horace's recuperation is continuing still. He and Lillian continue to squabble but they don't stay mad long. The strain of her parents and their kids never gave them much chance to be alone. The resentments that each had built up proved too much when they were first alone together. After they had suffered apart for a few years, the recognition of each's importance to the other was much clearer. They had been divorced in the meantime, and I am still waiting to hear that they have decided to tie the knot again.

Disability. Among more individual fears may be the loss of abilities that illness produces. The particular loss each person fears is different. A physician who has a stroke that impairs her memory may be severely depressed by this loss. Her inability to practice, her loss of emotional feedback and income derived from medicine amplify all the fears we have already discussed. A postal worker with the same disability may be forced into a retirement that will allow him to pursue the fishing he has always wished for. An artist with a stroke that affects his speech center may be relieved of the necessity to respond to questions when he would rather have people concentrate on his paintings. A salesperson with this type of stroke would be completely and permanently unemployable. The practical difficulties of each disability is unique. While some fear the loss of physical capacity, others fear the loss of intellectual function. An internist who has lost his leg will fare much better than the surgeon who has lost her arm.

Prestige and self-esteem. The woman who fears that the loss of her leg in an accident will repulse her husband when they are in bed together and the man who has become impotent as a consequence of an operation to cure his prostate cancer share a lot. They tie their self-esteem to physical attributes when their spouses and families value them for far more comprehensive qualities. The values of companionship and loyalty, compassion and honesty extend the boundaries of a relationship. They spread the blanket to include more facets of each's personality and weave the threads of the relationship in a more complicated and enduring pattern. The immediate gratification of a sexual relationship without attendant personal intimacy cannot. Our more encompassing human qualities smooth the dips and valleys of life's journey, giving support when troubles try to pull us down and augmenting the peaks for a greater measure of fulfillment.

Timing and Manner

Our fear of death and, indeed, our whole attitude toward death need regrounding in the truths well understood by previous generations.

Death is not defeat.
Death is not unnatural.
Death will come to us all.

That thought must be understood as a principle in everyone's life. Our deeds for good and bad will be judged when we are gone, if not by the Deity in the hereafter, then at least by the peers we leave behind. Few people do not care for their good name, and the reckless misery that a few perpetrate should well serve as a warning to any others so inclined. Most of us will succeed in leaving with a greater measure of good works to be remembered by those left behind.

If death is inevitable then the only issues we really need to consider are timing and manner. Medicine has succeeded dramatically in the fight against acute infections. The scourges of tuberculosis and pneumonia have been countered in many ways. Access to antibiotics has saved many millions of children from the deafness and pain of chronic ear infections. Childbirth is safer for both mother and child. Broken bones are repaired straighter and faster in youth and old age.

Yet for each success a problem appears. Lung cancer and heart disease are diseases of modern civilization. Automobile accidents kill more Americans than all but the top few cancers. AIDS has riveted our attention and inaugurated a national debate about our response to it. The lessons of Africa and the Caribbean show that the spread of this plague can permeate all levels of society. Neither occupation nor financial security can insulate us. These developments may sound depressing but understanding their evolution provides us with the tools to prevent them. Rather than reinforcing our impotence they show that if we take our individual and societal responsibilities seriously, we can find strategies to avoid them.

Cigarette smoking, the consumption of fats and salt and the increase of obesity are major factors for the production of heart disease, high blood pressure, diabetes and cancers of many sorts. Each of these factors is amenable to our individual intervention. We can, with proper education, choose a healthier course for ourselves. If we understand the priorities of our bodies and align those priorities with the priorities that we have as citizens, parents and spouses, we can have a major influence on the timing of our death.

If we wear automobile seatbelts, forego driving when we have been drinking and observe a reasonable speed limit, we can save, and lengthen, the lives of many thousands more. If we insist on glorifying a frontier approach to an urban life, we will have the deserved success of someone using a baseball bat as a tennis racket.

Our physical environment is different from a hundred years ago. The environment of a Kurdish shepherd is different from that of a New York financier. Yet we are dealing with pretty similar human beings from a biological standpoint. We all need to eat but not too much. We all need to sleep but again not too much. We need to work, to feel that we have accomplished something. We need to feel that someone loves us and will empathize with our pain. We need physical exercise but also protection from the elements. Neither intellect nor riches will change our biology. If we eat too much, drink too much, exercise too little and in general behave arrogantly—as if we were making the rules of life rather than having to abide by them—we will succeed only in shortening our time on this planet.

The rules of nature apply to us all. If we deprive our fellow man of air and light and clean water, we will have to pay as a society for the spread of tuberculosis, typhoid and plague. If we fail to show respect for our fellow man and allow him to be crowded in slums without an opportunity for useful work or adequate education, we will pay the price of drug and alcohol rehabilitation programs and the expenses of maintaining large prison populations.

If we believe we have an inalienable right to unprotected sex with multiple partners, we will continue to reap the rewards of sequential epidemics with syphilis, gonorrhea, herpes and AIDS. The problems are not new in human terms.

The diseases have different names and vary in the virulence and speed with which they attack, but the basic illness is the arrogant belief that the experience of a million years of human development somehow just doesn't apply to you.

Guess again! It does now, it has always in the past and will most certainly continue to apply in the future, no matter how artfully one may try to rationalize the contrary.

The good news is that if you can provide education to a group at risk, 80% will change their behavior to avoid the consequences. This was demonstrated after the transmission of AIDS was first understood.

The Communicable Disease Center follows the spread of many different diseases through different groups in our country. One such study was the spread and acquisition of hepatitis B in homosexuals. This is important because the lag time for the development of AIDS can be so long that it can be very difficult to track. However, it became well supported that the same kind of behaviors that spread hepatitis B also spread the AIDS virus.

If a behavioral change results in a reduction in the transmission of hepatitis B, it may be confidently assumed that the transmission of AIDS has also been reduced and this is exactly what happened. The CDC showed that after a widespread campaign to publicize knowledge about the transmission and prevention of AIDS, the spread of hepatitis B and AIDS decreased by 80%.

Not everyone is motivated to save himself and even with the best campaign there will be some who just don't get the message.

Nevertheless, if we could reduce the cancers of the lung and bladder by 80% with the elimination of cigarette smoking and postpone the deaths from heart disease with a diet and exercise prescription, it would be hailed as a miracle. But it is a miracle that is as possible as the reduction of the spread of hepatitis B in the gay community. They could succeed. Why can't the rest of us? Our lives are no less valuable and we are no less capable of self-discipline. We haven't yet gotten the message and it behooves us to hear it soon.

I really don't think that every premature death results from the inadequate efforts of the victim. We do not control nature. We try to uncover enough of its principles to follow them successfully. But we do not possess the clairvoyance to know them all or to measure all the variables to which we may be subject. Nevertheless, a major change in our attitudes about our responsibilities would pay substantial dividends.

If behavioral changes could improve the extent of healthy life by 60 or 70 per cent, this would be greater than any improvement which would ever result from heart transplants and more intensive care units.

Believing that we do not have to abide by the laws of nature and that a doctor can rescue us from our self-created foolishness with some medical miracle is an emotional adolescent fantasy. Unfortunately, it is a fantasy that has permeated all layers of American society. When we grow up enough to cast off this fantasy, we will be astonished by the power we really have.

We have seen that one facet of our fear of death has been a fear of how we get there. Pain, isolation, loss of autonomy are real issues on this journey, but they are issues that we can affect. You may not have much choice about the airline pilot taking you on vacation or the bus driver taking you to work but you have some choice about the physician guiding the trip of your life. Again, you have to do your homework. You have to have thought about what is important to you, what you want. The doctor shouldn't be working in a mental vacuum nor should you believe the doctor is a mind-reader. Speak your fears and values. Collaborate rather than abrogate your responsibilities!

Pain is not going to make us think more clearly or decide more wisely. It will not make us better people. Pain will distract us from communication and impede our thought. Pain is very personal. The doctor can't see it or measure it, but only listen to your report of it. But your report must be heard.

Not all pain should be treated the same way. Even the same pain need not be treated the same way every time. Nerve blocks, morphine, hypnosis all have a role in the relief of pain. How and when to use each is an art but an art that depends on accurate diagnosis at the outset.

A report of a stomach ache does *not* tell a doctor
whether you have a burst appendix, a kidney stone
or a cancer eating away a part of your spine.

Some patients may think that questioning their doctor about her views on pain relief will give them assurance. This is not necessarily so. Not many doctors are likely to say they are against relieving pain, nor are there many who are against it. Having a doctor say he is always quick to relieve pain may not be to your advantage if he doesn't take the time to find out what kind of pain you may be having, and then take the time to plan the best attack on it.

A chronic pain, whether from an arthritic back or cancer pressing on a nerve, is rarely best relieved by a shot of morphine. The effect soon wears off and the patient is left with both the renewed

pain and the side effects of the morphine. Anti-inflammatory medicines, nerve stimulators, cortisone injections or x-ray treatments
may all bring greater relief in the end.

**The acute pain of a kidney stone or the gasping of a patient
with lung cancer fighting for breath may only be relieved
by a large morphine injection, and no doctor should hesitate
to give this relief at these times.**

The Normality of Death

The issue of pain relief is central to the patient's concern about
the manner of his death. Most people do not want to die any sooner
than they have to. They cling to life with great ferocity. Most people
who wish for death are wishing for a relief from personal pain or
relief from the knowledge that their continued life presents a severe
emotional or financial burden to those for whom they care the most.
If we can relieve these concerns then we can extend the meaningful
life of the patient and loving communication with the family.

This is a more appropriate medical and human endeavor than
creating suicide machines and publishing instruction books on self-
destruction. Distorting the physician's role from preserving health and
life to one of administering death is a leap that I cannot make. To say
that death comes to us all and that it is the natural conclusion of life is
very different from recommending its premature appearance. Greater
attention to and research in the methods of pain relief will pay far larger human rewards. I would not shrink from using a pain relieving
treatment which might hasten a patient's death if the patient's pain
were otherwise unsurmountable, but, to me, the use of medicine to
produce death as its primary goal is a misuse of medicine.

NINA

I remember Nina, a physician's widow with advanced
cancer of the pancreas. She was only 60, but she had suffered many medical catastrophes before this. I had treated her for the complications of severe emphysema, terri-

ble shortness of breath and many pneumonias. She had suffered collapsed lungs and infections in the pleural space surrounding the lungs. There were many times when the interns and residents at the hospital thought I was foolish for discharging her to her own home instead of sending her to a nursing home. But I knew her commitment to life and her children and I depended on her collaboration in following the rehabilitation program which was prescribed.

When the pancreatic cancer was finally diagnosed, the emotional blow to Nina was terrible. Although she fought her emphysema with great determination, she knew the cancer had spread enough that she would not be victorious. In addition, the pain was increasing daily and was enough to occupy her mind completely. Nina began to ask me to give her medicines to kill herself.

The severity of her breathing problems would have made accomplishment simple. Instead, I searched for someone who might be able to help her in a more substantial way. Pain management was not considered a speciality in those days, but I learned that one of our anesthesiology professors was working with certain types of spinal nerve blocks. I asked him to see Nina. She seemed a good candidate but her lung disease presented the possibility of some dangerous complications.

The professor and I went over the possibilities with Nina very carefully. She chose to let us try. Fortunately it worked. She achieved 90% relief within the first six hours and it continued until her death five weeks later. After she was out of pain, she said to me, "John, I really didn't want to die. I have so much left to take care of. I have to arrange the house and financial affairs so that the younger children can finish college and that their trustees know exactly what I want done for them. But I couldn't live any longer with that pain. It was 'screech-

SOULMEDICINE

ing terrible' every minute, every second. I would have done anything to get rid of it."

Nina died at home, pain-free. She did not live long but the additional weeks were important to her to put her things in order and they were especially important to her children who had a chance to say goodbye. Their father had died of a sudden unexpected heart attack, and their grief had been increased by that inability to have said goodbye to him. Successful pain management was preferable to assisted death, preferable to the family and especially preferable to the patient. The resources necessary were not high- tech. It took an intelligent, caring man and a long needle. I am grateful that I found him.

Nina was sick enough to have died in the hospital. She had breathing problems as well as the digestive troubles that come with pancreatic cancer. She would have qualified for hospital admission even by today's criteria. She had no desire to be in the hospital. She knew she was going to die. Her family knew she was going to die. There was no magic belief that being in a hospital was going to prevent her death. But there was the understanding that being in the hospital would prevent her family from being with her as much as they were. Being at home allowed her family to do the many little things that expressed their love for her and she for them. Her pain had been taken care of. We had arranged for oxygen tanks so she could get around. I visited weekly to see her progress and once drew blood to see if a treatable complication had occurred. There was nothing more that would have been accomplished had she been in the hospital.

If dying at home is preferable, why do so many people die in hospitals?

Pain management is one reason. It is easier to put someone in the hospital and give them a shot than to put together a program of pain tablets or suppositories to be managed at home. Sometimes injections are truly necessary but if families can be taught to give insulin injections, there is no reason that they cannot be taught to give pain injections.

Skilled nursing care to avoid additional pain and complication is available in hospitals but also at home through the Visiting Nurses Association. Physicians are more easily available in the hospital but what one needs here is not emergency care but a thoughtful plan. This can be provided by physician home visits just as by the nurses.

The real reason most people die in hospitals is the reluctance to confront the fact and normality of death by the patient's family and physician. The patient generally is aware that he is dying. He may enter into a conspiracy of silence with his family if he sees this fact upsetting them too much, but this should not be interpreted as ignorance on his part.

As we have discussed, the patient's death will be very painful for the family on many levels. Death itself is painful for the family because if the patient can die then, they, the family, can die too. The family may also be squeamish about the mystery and physical reality of death. With proper education this can usually be overcome. In addition, the physician has a stake in denying death. Despite the obvious reality that we will all die, the physician may look on the patient's death as a defeat. If a doctor looks at her job as keeping the patient alive, then the patient's death is certainly irrefutable evidence of her impotence.

If a doctor looks at her job as helping a patient have as comfortable and meaningful life for as long as possible, then death is not defeat but the conclusion of a job, hopefully well done.

This should not be taken as an indication that the physician will not mourn the patient. The relationship that can develop between a physician and patient at this time is something special. The physician must take professional and human satisfaction in knowing that he cared enough to do the job the best that anyone could and to have pro-

vided the opportunity for the patient to resolve any existing ambivalence with the people near to him. This is not defeat.

Another aspect of dying at home is that it prevents the
patient's isolation. Large hospitals are ideally designed for the effi-
cient performance of a variety of medical procedures. Hip replace-
ments, coronary by-pass surgery, cancer surgery all need an experienced smooth functioning team for the best results. While some
consideration has to be given to the individual variation of patients,
the emphasis will necessarily be on their homogeneity. The overall
results will be best if all participants know their steps in the carefully choreographed production.

This situation is not well designed for the patient who is not
having such surgery, particularly the patient for whom the goal of
cure has been superseded by the goal of comfort. Visiting rules and
medication programs designed so that physical therapy and other
predictable needs of the surgical patients can be met are antithetical
to the needs of the other patients.

Our patients need maximum autonomy and as little hindrance
to the coming and going of family. Since they are not part of the upbeat
"fix'em and get'em out" surgical team, our patients begin to feel isolated because they have different needs, a different schedule and different goals. The staff may feel depressed by seeing patients for whom
they think they can do nothing. The staff may also feel that catering to
these patients' needs diverts them from their primary task of caring
for patients who are going to "get well and go home." Despite the bus-
tle and activity of the hospital floor, our patients may experience
increasing loneliness as staff stop coming into the room.

**The issues of isolation, loneliness, lack of autonomy and
control are characteristic of a large hospital and the
opposite of home care during this time.**

At home, the patient is the only medical priority; there is no
need to compete. She is in the midst of family; no one can ignore her.
In addition, she can still be useful. She may answer the telephone,

watch the grandchildren or relay messages for other family members. She gives as well as takes and remains an integral element in the fabric of the family. Fear is dissipated by familiarity. Children learn that death is the normal outcome of life and that love endures. The more concrete and predictable we can make a situation, the more effectively we diffuse fear. In the uncertainty of our final days, this is often best done at home.

You may want to remember:

✦ Fears are real and sometimes more threatening than death to certain sufferers.

✦ Fear grows with uncertainty and speculation about the unknown.

✦ Describing pain as clearly as you can will help a doctor make the best diagnosis for you.

- Where does the pain start?
- Is the pain steady or does it come and go?
- Does the pain last for a long time or does it stab at you briefly?
- Does the pain move from one part of the body to another in a regular way?
- Is it better when you are still or when you move around?
- Is there a position that makes it better? Worse?
- Is there a time of day when it is better? Worse?
- What treatments have you tried?
- Have they helped?

There are many other questions a doctor may ask. It is important for your doctor to examine you to see what maneuvers may alleviate or worsen the pain. Only then can he be confident with a diagnosis on which to base treatment.

CHAPTER TEN

Grief and Resolution

America has tried to outlaw grief. When bad things happen, we are supposed to get over them fast and get back to our lives. Financial ruin, natural catastrophe, international terrorism and death merely represent transient opportunities for us to demonstrate the American capacity to forget quickly. Dwelling on these events is morbid and depressing and we can't do anything about them anyway, so why think about them at all?

Our national propensity for short memory is at serious odds with our human needs. To equate the tragedies of our individual lives with the sensationalist mayhem depicted nightly in our living rooms under the guise of "news" is a terrible mistake.

Our Ambivalent Responses

The loss of a job, our home or a parent has a very real impact on the way we view the world and ourselves. As with any human reaction, the psychic planes on which we respond are multiple and not ever lined up in an orderly array.

As we have seen in previous chapters, human beings have the ability and the predilection to feel ambivalently about many aspects of our lives—some important and others trivial. Our job may be enjoyable or boring. Often our sense of self-esteem and importance is tied to our occupation. Most of us do not do it for free and we depend on our work-derived income to support our families. Nevertheless, we may dislike our boss or the hours we work or the commute required to get there. If only we had a chance to start over, we would do things differently.

Suddenly, the economy falters, our employer fails and, lo and behold, we are out of work. Now, we are forced to start over. Are we happy? Usually not. The loss of income when faced with a mort-gage and car payments considerably dampens our sense of adventure. Nevertheless there is a tingling of excitement that accompanies our job search. The uncertainty of new possibilities can be exhila-rating. Such is human ambivalence.

Grief has many aspects. One of them is ambivalence. Learning to accept and resolve that ambivalence is a key feature of the struggle through grief. The loss of a parent or child is a profoundly sad experi-ence. If it happens quickly and unexpectedly, there may be little ambivalence. There was little or no suffering and the loss is unalloyed.

As the period of illness lengthens and the intensity of suffer-ing increases, we begin to appreciate a complexity of feelings about our loss. The pain of our loss begins to be offset on one level by the pain of the patient. Our reluctance to let go is countered by the patient's acceptance that the time is soon. The intensity of our pain is just as great at the loss but we begin to recognize that there are other dimensions that we care about as well. The scream of our despair is softened by the patient's echo of acquiescence.

None of us is perfect and who is most aware of our imperfec-tions than those who are closest to us? Parents and children often have special reasons for minimizing each other's "warts," but a spouse or sibling does not. Living together requires compromise whether as chil-dren or adults. Some compromises may be trivial and easily forgotten but many are not. Any allocation of scarce resources, time or money, means that someone gets a little bigger piece and someone a little smaller, and in no case can either get the whole pie. This truism fre-quently leads to the harmless fantasy of what it might be like if the other were not there to compete. Usually this passes quickly. Both chil-dren and adults have limited memories for these transient fancies and the realities of interdependence soon prevail.

Not everyone compromises with the same degree of grace and sometimes one tries too much to gain advantage from an inevitable capitulation. Alternatively, one may press an advantage too hard and deny something the other holds very dear. Depending upon circumstance and personality, the memory of these slights may be increased in number and importance by the passage of years. This increase is amplified by proximity and diminished by distance. As brothers and sisters establish their own homes, the tensions diminish while a long married couple may remember every fight as if it were yesterday. The expression of grief in these situations can be complicated by a sense of relief.

Recognizing your spouse's "warts" is not being disloyal. Some of those characteristics which you find most upsetting may be funny or endearing to others not exposed to them as constantly as you are. Some may be expressions of the same personality traits which you most admire. Being honest about your spouse's "warts" may even stimulate you to consider your own.

I have often been startled by the change that takes place after the loss of a spouse in a tempestuous marriage. When I was much younger, I would anticipate a visit from the bereaved spouse expecting to hear that there had been a tremendous reduction in the stress of life since the survivor no longer had to put up with all the previously lamented faults. An early visit may in fact contain such an admission.

The startling change begins about the second or third month after the loss. Slowly the volume of complaints declines and the good memories begin to be asserted. No longer was Sam more devoted to his car than his spouse. He is remembered for having kept everything in perfect working order. Diana is no longer a nagging penny-pincher. She is praised for having been able to stretch a modest income with great imagination.

MEL'S BELLOWING

Mel was a bombastic genius of an engineer. His huge size and satanic white goatee were as arresting as his bellowing voice. He grew up poor and worked his way through college playing trumpet in a local jazz band. Self-promotion was always his strong suit and it served him well as a performer and later as the chief salesman for the heavy equipment that his company manufactured. His wife, Louise, in complete contrast, was petite and gentle. She had grown up in more affluent circumstances and was attracted by someone who had the strength to stand up to her intimidating family. Besides, Mel was a lot of fun. He was always the life of the party, and when he became successful there was plenty of excitement as they travelled around the world—to Hong Kong, Buenos Aires, Paris—entertaining his clients.

By the time I met Mel he was long retired and in his 70s. His large size had resulted in substantial arthritis of the spine and main joints, and he had great difficulty getting around. The one organ that had not diminished its activity was his mouth. He would still yell with gusto and self-importance. Instead of an office full of cringing employees, his audience was reduced to Louise and a faithful, long-suffering nurse.

Louise would try to escape by sitting in another room and feigning deafness. After his bellowing requests remained unanswered, Mel would heave himself out of his chair and stagger into the hall with his gnarled Scottish walking stick. Only the comatose would have been able to ignore his requests at that point and Louise would scurry to him, afraid that he would fall and injure himself.

I first saw this performance when, after having become the family doctor a few years before, I visited their apartment. Mel had contracted a severe case of the flu and all were concerned that pneumonia had complicated the picture. Mel recovered from this illness and I did not see him for almost a year, satisfying his requests via telephone. Unfortunately when Louise next called, Mel had fallen. He had been going to the bathroom that night and tripped over his slipper.

I accompanied him in the ambulance to the hospital emergency room where the x-ray confirmed that his hip was indeed broken. This was complicated by blood clots from his leg veins, bleeding ulcers aggravated by blood-thinning medications and Mel's increasing immobility because he refused to make a move if he could induce someone else to do it for him. Mel also refused to see a psychiatrist or cooperate with any treatment directed at his obvious depression. "I'm old and I'm tired and I have enough money to pay people to do whatever I want, so what do I need a psychiatrist for? You need a psychiatrist for not seeing it!"

Finally, Mel was strong enough to take home. Although it had been quieter at home, Louise was so exhausted from running back and forth to the hospital every day that she was actually anxious to get him back. A hospital bed had been set up in the library and extra nurses hired to attend to him 'round the clock. A physical therapy program was begun but ended when it was clear that Mel had lost any interest in getting out of bed as long as people would serve him.

This performance continued until he had his first stroke eight months later. An ambulance was called and Mel was brought back to the hospital. He had a couple of rough days but the paralysis was on his left side and his speech was unaffected. He moved less but he yelled with undiminished belligerence. When he got home again, he was increasingly intolerant of Louise's absences and would bellow invectives until she appeared. The more he was restricted, the more he tried to imprison her.

Several smaller strokes occurred. He could still talk but he made less sense. These strokes affected his thinking. The strain on Louise increased. She was only a year younger than her husband, but she smoked more and ate less. She lost weight and finally one morning the nurse called me to say that Louise was in the bathroom vomiting blood.

Another trip in the ambulance ensued—this one without Mel. Louise had developed a bleeding ulcer which took a week of hospitalization to stabilize. As I was ready to send her home, she broke into sobs.

"I can't go back there again. It's like living in a bus station. If Mel isn't yelling for me, one of the nurses needs me for something. When I go to bed I hear him screaming and when I wake up I hear it. Everybody complains that hospitals are noisy but this has been the quietest time I've had in months. I have made up my mind, Mel has to go to the nursing home. We can afford a nice one and if he doesn't, I'll end up dead and no one will be around to take care of him."

With her plan firmly in mind Louise was much more at ease when she went home. The next week she told Mel she had to go back to the hospital for a test but went to visit nursing homes with her lawyer instead. She came back elated. She had found just the place in a nearby suburb and she wanted me to check its medical reputation to assure herself that it would be suitable. I did and it was. She arranged for his admission.

It was a couple of weeks before a bed became available and Louise busied herself getting the things together that she imagined Mel would need, as if he were off on a business trip again. She had decided that she was not going to tell Mel anything until everything was set. She didn't know if she could stand up to his refusal, and she wanted to give herself every chance.

At last, word came that a bed was available and Louise was asked to bring Mel the following day. I wasn't present when Louise told Mel but she later reported that his voice was strong as ever. She never backed down. The memory of all the blood she lost firmed her resolve. I never saw Mel again. His care was transferred to a doctor in the town near the nursing home who could visit on a regular basis if it should be necessary. I saw Louise more regularly after that.

She came in to check her blood count and make sure that there was no further bleeding from the ulcer which was quiescent. She would always tell me news of Mel and how well he had adjusted to his new environment. As the months passed, Louise began to relate that she sometimes felt lonely in the big old apartment. Mel's old nurse would stay over a few nights a week just to keep her company. Although it was a big production to get to the home, she looked forward more and more to the weekly visits to see him.

Our Selective Memory

About a year later, my secretary buzzed me to say that Louise was on the phone. When I picked up all I heard was sobbing. Finally Louise choked out that Mel had died the previous night. He must have had another stroke. He was dead when the nurse came 'round to check him. I told her how sorry I was to hear the news and that I understood how sad she must feel.

When she came to see me for her next visit, Louise was profoundly bereaved. The years she had trembled to his demands and shouting were forgotten. The bleeding ulcer was forgotten. His blustering intransigence at going to the nursing home was forgotten. She remembered only the good times. The trips, the fun, the gaiety were vivid, and all else was forgotten. Her loneliness and grief were inconsolable. She rehearsed again every minute detail of her last visit to him as if that formula should conjure his reappearance.

This became a ritual for each visit. I was one of the few people left who knew how wonderful he was. All of their friends had died and she had only a niece in Florida as her last relative. After a few months and with winter approaching, Louise decided that she couldn't bear living in the apartment that she and Mel had shared. The memories made her too sad. She packed up and moved to Florida near her niece.

I received a card a few years later from her niece telling me that Louise had developed a severe pneumonia following the flu and died as she was waiting to be admitted to the hospital. She had never stopped telling everyone she met how wonderful her husband had been and how much she missed him still. That was many years ago. I remember Louise fondly and I remember well the lesson she taught me about the quirks of the human memory, particularly when they relate to grief.

The selectivity of memory helps us all. We remember less the pain of our parent's last weeks than the bravery and inspiration which we so admired. We remember the look of quiet joy after a visit from the grandchild on a weekend break from school.

One aspect of the grieving process is the replacement of immediate sadness by cherished good memories—which are the ones that last forever.

It is good to be able to laugh about and recognize the fallibility of all human beings without forgetting those characteristics that made the lost one so special. How long this takes is very individual but the usual range is six to eighteen months.

A sense of guilt is the most difficult and most important to resolve. The sudden death of someone from whom you may be estranged necessarily prevents you from healing that estrangement. If the person is one by whom you suffered terrible harm and with whom you have little other relation, hearing about his death may have a minimal negative effect on you. On the other hand, if you haven't spoken to your father or sister for years since a monumental family blow-up, their death has a very different import. These are not relationships that can be dismissed without pain. Whatever was done to create the division has to be balanced against the intensity of early childhood bonding. You have only one father and no matter how horrible a wrong he may have perpetrated, there is a corner of your being that still loves him.

Having been denied the chance to say good-bye or to try once again to resolve alienation perpetuates a never-healing wound. Perhaps worse is knowing of a lingering illness and having the opportunity but not taking the initiative to resolve the hurt.

Also unfortunate is misreading the signs and complaints so that an opportunity is presented but misunderstood. These particular issues represent such an important source of avoidable misery, I would be remiss not to emphasize them.

The difficulty of resolving grief and completing a mourning process in the presence of a serious division or guilt is so great that I do not think it can be done successfully without real professional help of either a psychiatric or spiritual sort. Without it the emotional chaos which is being covered over must erupt a hundred times in ways that will be destructive to the life and relationship of a survivor. This can serve to perpetuate the kinds of suffering which initiated the family break in the first place. Resolution will break the cycle.

Anger can play a major role in normal grief. It is an emotion many bereaved people are embarrassed to express. They may feel their loss is in some way deserved or their fault, and how could they have the effrontery to feel anger. Bad things happen and often there is no one to blame.

**Not to be able to express appropriate anger
retards the resolution we need to live a healthy life.
How we deal with that anger may predict
how successfully we resume our lives.**

MARY'S PREGNANCY

Mary was elated to learn she was pregnant. How wrong that doctor had been. She had gone to the gynecologist for a checkup because she wanted to become pregnant. A cheerless frown came over him as he told her that scarring from her burst appendix many years before made getting pregnant an unlikely possibility.

She was the last sister to become pregnant. All the others were so prolific, she sometimes thought they were competing to see who could produce the most offspring. She was the only one to have a serious career outside the family, and that made her feel different.

Mary was very bright, and when she worked hard she clearly accomplished a lot. The brokerage firm for which she worked recognized this and she advanced quickly. Nevertheless she felt out of step with her family. They couldn't understand why she worked so much and didn't try to settle down.

Finally, ten years later she did fall in love with someone who was terrific and did not find her accomplishments strange or threatening. They got married and, as she was getting older, she was anxious to get pregnant. The doctor's remark about her prospective fertility was a terrible blow but she had overcome difficulties before and was confident she could again. It took longer than she had anticipated and there had been a miscarriage along the way, but now she was in her seventh month and happy as could be. Nothing stood in her way.

The pregnancy was relatively easy. After the first months of nausea she felt filled with life—her own and the baby's. The delivery was uneventful and a perfect little boy came into their lives. The first months were busy: learning to be a mother, breast feeding, diapering, getting up in the middle of the night, sometimes being too tired to think but never to feel.

Then the white heat explosion, the atomic nightmare, the Humpty Dumpty life never to be put back together again. Little Sam had a cough. It got worse that night.

What could it be? He didn't have a fever but he couldn't lie down. He wouldn't go to sleep. At eight o'clock she called Dr. Moss the pediatrician. Can't think what he has, better bring him in and let me get a look . . . fluid in the lungs . . . heart murmur . . . better get him to the hospital to see what the matter is . . . needs an emergency heart operation . . . terrible odds . . . second opinion agrees . . . no time to wait. I'm so sorry. His heart was so small. There was nothing to do. There was no way to know he had that problem. We couldn't have fixed it even if we had known sooner. I am so sorry. Everybody tried their best . . .

Mary sat numb on the stained polyester-covered foam rubber couch. The smell of other worried parents' stale cigarette smoke rose from its cracks. The gray brown dawn crept along the window. She couldn't feel her husband holding her, sobbing. She died, not Sam, not that perfect pink baby. Not that perfect gift that she had wanted so badly and deserved so much after all her troubles. She died. She wished to be dead. She deserved to be dead. Not Sam, never Sam. Oh, no, no, no.

She made them let her see him. All blue now, those tubes all over, no cough, no crying, no life. The next days a blur. The baby clothes for the burial. The church full of people. Few had ever seen that perfect little baby lying in that little mahogany box. No tears for the public. My loss, my pain. What do they know? Their children are alive—all of them. We are so sorry . . . so sorry . . . God's plan . . . God's will . . . the innocent go right to heaven . . . STUPID . . . STUPID . . . STUPID. God had no plan for little Sam, the perfect baby . . . he doesn't need Sam in heaven. I need him here. All those people mouthing platitudes, sad but thankful its not them, their baby, their son, their daughter. Why me? Why my baby?

The speed of events had left Mary no time for thought. The

shocks were unrelieved in ever-increasing horror. The ultimate cul-mination was devastating beyond the capacity of human imagina-tion. When the funeral was over and people had gone away, Mary and her husband, Howard, were left sitting alone in their living room staring at each other. They could not believe what had hap-pened or that it had happened to them. There was no way that they could react in a human way. They were in a trance. They did not know what to say to each other or even to think themselves.

Anger and Loss

The stages that the bereaved pass through are similar to those described by Dr. Elizabeth Kubler-Ross for the patient faced with a fatal diagnosis. The first stages of shock and denial had passed quickly for Mary and Howard and they were so busy during those hours that there was little time to dwell on those aspects. The stage of anger was more complex. This is a facet of the human condition which goes back to the book of Job. It has been considered by every ethicist, philosopher and clergyman who has ever thought. I have been particularly impressed by the wisdom of Rabbi Harold Kushner whose own loss of a young son triggered a reflection grounded in honest human emotion. He has collected his thoughts in a book entitled *When Bad Things Happen to Good People.*

Survivors are usually uncomfortable with their anger. There is a universal feeling that in some way they were responsible for the tragedy. If they had made a demand or not made a demand, or helped or not helped, that in some way things would have been different.

This guilt appears to have its origins in a human need to under-stand the patterns which govern the workings of nature. We have a need to believe that the world makes sense. If it does and there is a rea-son for everything, it is an easy step to believe that something we have done has resulted in this tragedy. A fuller spiritual and philosophical treatment of these issues is far beyond the scope of this book.

It suffices to recognize that the pain of the loss is amplified by a feeling of responsibility which is really inappropriate.

**The expression of anger has a role in the healing of a loss.
The failure to acknowledge this role is a serious hindrance
to the resolution of the grief.**

Mary and Howard bottled up their unexpressed anger. Who could they blame? Each other? Each suffered silently. They avoided going into Sam's room. They tried in some way to pretend that it hadn't happened. They were also astonished by the reaction of some of their friends. While they weren't completely ignored, interactions were the most perfunctory and superficial. This only reenforced Mary and Howard's fear that they had in some way been responsible for Sam's death. They did not realize that their tragedy had been so awful that their friends could not deal with it either.

The terrible unspoken fear of every parent is the death of a child. Mary and Howard's friends needed to separate themselves from the horrible thing that had happened. By pushing it out of their minds, by trying to in some way to distinguish their lives from those of Mary and Howard, they might be able to soften the fear that this could happen to them too. This last mechanism lay behind the platitudes that so hurt and infuriated Mary at the funeral. The invocation of God's will, or plan, or mercy were not only attempts to find a coherence in the world but also to somehow separate the speaker from the bereaved.

The grief-stricken are not the only ones subject to such a psychological assault. A patient may find himself subjected to relentless questioning by acquaintances and co-workers. While the apparent concern is for the patient, the real, if unconscious, motivation is to find some feature to differentiate the questioner from the patient. He needs some way to pretend that such illness cannot happen to him.

This is a situation in which the family can run interference. There is no requirement that the self-serving questioning must be satisfied. It is adequate to resort to vague generalities or to the current uncertainty of the doctors. Do not waste your emotional energy on those whose interest is feigned. The true friend will ask what he can do for you and leave the details of your illness to a time when you want to talk.

Guilt and isolation suppress healthy anger. They inhibit the resolution of your grief that you need to carry on. Your life has been torn apart. You have suffered a terrible loss. This was done to you. It was not your fault. What kind of person would accept such a wrong meekly? Why shouldn't you scream and cry? Nothing will bring back your world. It is gone forever. You may be able to build a new one but only if you are able to sweep the remnants from the foundation which you will need to try again. Admitting the anger helps that healing process.

There are many sources of anger. You may be angry that your husband had three too many drinks before he got in the car and ran off the road and into the river where he drowned. You may be angry that the bartender sold him the drinks which clouded his judgment when he got in the car. You may be angry with his physician who had failed to get him to agree to enter an alcoholic detox program.

In different circumstances you may be angry with your husband for smoking the cigarettes that caused his lung cancer, or with the drunk driver who caused the accident in which your mother was killed. The anger in these situations has an identifiable target on which you can focus. This sometimes makes it easier to shed the guilt and avoid the isolation, but guilt and isolation will not be far under the surface.

Sometimes a motivation for suing the bartender or the doctor is to fight "survivor's guilt" and reaffirm, especially to ourselves, that it was not our fault.

Mary and Howard had no such convenient focus for their anger. Since the time of Job it has been thought imprudent to be angry with God. Not having anyone on whom to lay off guilt, they kept it for themselves and it festered. They didn't speak, didn't hold each other or express their love in any other physical way. They kept their pain inside because they didn't know what to do with it. They did go to see one psychiatrist but he was not attuned to the pain of grieving young parents and they did not feel enough of a connection to keep going. They had some counseling sessions with their minister but he kept reiterating the mystery of God's plan for the world, which did not provide much help in resolving their anger or sadness.

This is a time of great danger both for the parents individually and for their marriage. This is a time when depression may deepen to the point of suicide, either to escape the bleakness of this world or to join the child in the next. It is also a time when marriages break up. Being together reminds each partner of the terrible pain that they share.

Breaking up a marriage at this point does not lead to a better resolution of the grief. It frequently retards even more the resolution because the partners become sidetracked by the business of splitting up and seeking new mates. They stay occupied with "busy work" which allows them to blot out the memory for the moment. But their every thought, every action or inaction is dominated by unresolved grief. Better to deal with it as a unit and then decide that the marriage is no longer vital.

With the help of some friends, Mary and Howard did find a therapist who had particular expertise in the bereavement of young parents, and they began the long road back. The resolution was successful because Mary and Howard were and are committed to each other as individuals and themselves as a family. They got good help and were able to express not only anger but love. They have subsequently had a little daughter whom they love very much. She is not a substitute for Sam, but a very special person in her own right. The sadness that Mary and Howard feel when they think of Sam is now tempered by the good memories that they have kept of him and how much they loved him.

As Mary worked to resolve her grief, she sought to help others who were in her situation. Often people who have felt the intensity of pain and have found an approach to alleviate it will feel obligated to help shorten the suffering of others. Mary has worked tirelessly at her local hospital to make the professional staff more sensitive to the issues of bereaved young parents and how to facilitate the resolution of their grief. She has been available at any time to anyone who suffers a similar loss and has helped put them in touch with specialized professional help quickly. As someone who has "been there and back," she knows how to give form to the inchoate pain and help her fellow parents find the way to resolution.

When Len Bias died of a cocaine overdose on the eve of a much heralded career in professional basketball, his family was struck by the same terrible pain and loss that Mary and Howard suffered. His mother, Lenise, made the same kind of courageous decision to devote herself to preventing the pain of other mothers. She became a tireless crusader against drugs. As someone who has an important story to tell from her own life, she has a credibility which reinforces her message fiercely to her listeners.

Besides the satisfaction of helping people, Mary and Lenise have an ongoing sense of connection with the lost child. This connection gives life to the child's memory long after he has died.

The resolution of grief can take many forms.
No two people suffer in the same way even if they
are suffering the loss of the same person.

There is no place for competition in real grief. Your grief is valid on its own merits. It does not have to be more than mine. Our losses cause each of us pain and in that community of pain we may find a foundation on which to comfort and support each other. We can help remember each other's loss by listening to each other's stories. We can tell our own stories about the lost one. We can remember the love that each showed for the other, the way that he depended on you, or how he could anticipate when you were sad or happy. We give life to the memory by remembering.

Some think that the job of the condolence visit is to take the bereaved's mind off the loss. Nothing could be more wrong. By remembering, by speaking the lost one's name, by telling the stories again and again, the lost one returns to life. At least enough so that peace can be made with the loss. Talking about the weather or last night's ball game serves no purpose.

A person has died. Someone who has touched your life enough for you to be at the home has died. That is the best focus of discussion and memory. If this leads to tears, that is an expression of real emotion and helps all the bereaved. Don't be afraid or embarrassed to cry. It helps others know that they share a loss. They are not alone.

When someone dies, I almost never prescribe sedatives for the family. Sedatives attenuate the intensity of feelings which ultimately lead to the resolution of grief.

If you prevent the survivor from feeling his true emotions, you interfere with his ability to weave a solution to his pain.

Sedatives reinforce an idea that somehow it is wrong to express our most powerful feelings. Yet unless we express these feelings and admit their validity we can never work through our grief and resume our lives. The unresolved anger, ambivalence and grief will continue to distort our feelings and behavior forever. They will result in prolonged depression and erratic moods and responses when we least expect it. We will be forced to pay a high price for this distortion of our feelings, and those we love will also be forced to pay a price since our responses to them will also be strained.

I am struck by the strong feelings of loss that those of us feel who have lost parents when we are already grown. The loss of a parent is painful at any age. I have seen senior executives suffer terribly because they refused to admit even to themselves the pain of losing a 90-year-old mother. We believe that because we have been lucky enough to have a parent share our maturity, we should not grieve with equal intensity. And that is wrong. The fact that she lived a good life, or had been in pain and now is relieved, does not diminish the sense of loss. That we may bear this pain quietly does not diminish its intensity.

I was seeing Charles for his yearly physical and casually asked about his mother, whom I knew had a broken hip the previous year. I had seen Charles a few months before for an acute problem but we had not had much opportunity to talk. When he told me she had died suddenly six months ago, I felt his loss. I was at first surprised and somewhat hurt that he had not told me of her death at that last visit, but then I thought again of my own responses the year before.

My involvement with my mother's care and final months had been so intense. I was proud of what we had accomplished together and I was very saddened by her loss. But I felt my grief as a very private feeling. I did not feel it was the subject of casual conversation. It was too important to me. I know some friends who were upset to have learned of her death from someone other than me. I was sorry but I couldn't discuss it then. I found that sometimes I did not even want to read the condolence notes when they arrived. Yet as the months passed, as the weariness of the experience retreated and the wonderful memories of her wit, strength and bravery remained, I found I wanted to reread those letters, and I was very anxious to write back and tell those friends how much I really appreciated their sentiments.

There is a season for crying and a season for laughing and if one waits, the time for each will come.

Another way some people find expression for their grief is to follow some interest of his. This can be maintaining a particular rose bush with care or visiting a particular place where he felt particularly at home. It can mean supporting a particular charity, not just with money but with a commitment and personal effort.

It can mean finishing a book or painting or a job he started. It can mean wearing a piece of jewelry or an article of clothing he frequently wore or carried. The specific expression is important only insofar as it maintains the desired connection. Each of the situations we have discussed serves that purpose. Mary helped others who suffer as she did. Lenise crusades against the kind of death her son suffered. Louise remembers the good and forgets the difficult.

What can we do when our friends suffer a loss?

✦ Acknowledge how much pain your friend is in.
Don't tell him he will get over it. Hopefully he will,
but your exhortation will not speed the process.

✦ Don't tell him the lost one is better off and out of
suffering. If it is true, he knows it but it is irrelevant to
his pain right then.

✦ Let him express his real sorrow without feeling a need
to justify it.

✦ Grief is not competitive, don't tell him about someone
who suffered more. His grief is unique to him and he is
not interested in comparison.

✦ Let him know how his loved one depended on him
and loved him.

✦ Tell him your own stories about the loved one so that
the memories can build on each other.

✦ Don't be afraid to mention the person's name.
A condolence visit is about resolving grief and honoring
the dead, not about discussing trivialities.

✦ Let your friend know he was not responsible for his loved
one's death. This may seem obvious to you but at a time of
loss, the mind can work in strange ways and "survivor's
guilt" is a powerful force.

✦ Let your friend know how terrible you know his loss
to be and that he did not deserve it.

✦ Tell your friend you love him and feel so bad about
his pain.

CHAPTER ELEVEN

*What to Expect
From Your Doctor*

In our journey we have visited many individuals and many families. We have seen how they have made decisions in times of sickness. We have seen how they have reacted emotionally to the results of their decisions. For both patients and families, two factors have been important in achieving a sense of triumph in situations of such uncertainty: goals and a guide.

In an earlier chapter we discussed in great detail the issues of setting goals. Subsequent chapters chronicled the goals that others have set as well as assessing how closely they may have come to accomplishing them.

The factor of the guide has only been alluded to as we have considered the role of physicians in illness. Much of this book has been written with the expectation that the reader will not have an experienced family doctor on whom he can rely in times of medical disaster. Unfortunately this is frequently true and you may often feel pushed around by institutional priorities or intimidated by well meaning but remote specialists. When 70% of American physicians are specialists and only 30% are primary care practitioners (family doctors, GPs, pediatricians or general internists), it is often difficult to achieve the balance between technology and patient needs that results in good medical care.

Our search for a guide is complicated by the relative scarcity of doctors eager to function in that capacity. Unfortunately, some who may be willing may not be up to it. While newspapers and television shows usually feature the more dramatic errors of technology gone astray, no segment of medicine is immune from the presence of bad apples.

Distinguishing Between Good and Bad

Most people would think of a bad doctor as one who is inept or doesn't come up with the right treatment or prescription. Some bad results are the consequence of physician ineptitude. Good physicians will have a higher likelihood of good results than those who are less intelligent or less committed to keeping up with new developments.

Serious illness is an uncertain undertaking. Bad results do not necessarily mean that the physician is personally bad or inept. Even the most intelligent and well-informed doctor will come up against conditions in which the course or response to treatment is going to turn out badly. This is the nature of medicine. Human knowledge has obvious limitations to our understanding of the physical and psychic responses of patients to illness.

Some of the difference between good and bad doctors is how they react when things go badly.

Losing your cool, blaming others or disappearing are all bad. Trying to help the patient and family choose alternative goals, enlisting the help of other professionals who can contribute, and showing a commitment to the patient whatever the outcome are all good.

Motivated by greed. This is probably more common than doctors like to admit but less than the media would have us believe. Whatever the reason, physicians who see you as a wallet walking through their offices are physicians to be avoided. Physicians who perform a lot of tests, whether blood tests, x-rays or procedures for which they are paid have a serious conflict of interest.

Are the tests really necessary or does the physician habitually use them because they help pay the office overhead?

In some cases, having the tests available may speed diagnosis or result in lower costs because you need not go somewhere else to obtain them. In some remote areas, the physician's office may be the only place to obtain them without serious hardship. Nevertheless, offices in which testing has a higher priority than examining or talking to patients need to justify this approach.

Financial gain. An especially repugnant extension of this is the referral of patients to specific laboratory facilities, x-ray scanners, nursing homes or home care programs in which the physician is a silent financial partner. Happily, this is one area in which legislation has been passed making this practice illegal as well as immoral.

Sexual or physical abuse. From the time of Hippocrates, physicians have been prohibited by law, professional rules and moral precept from having sexual relations with their patients. Yet, because of fatigue, poor judgment or mental defect, some physicians have been guilty of this behavior. A physician who makes lewd remarks or suggests meeting outside of the professional relationship should be shunned. Notifying your local medical society is an important step to protect others from the advances of such a misguided doctor. A physician who demonstrates such poor judgment could hardly be trusted to manage a complex illness for you or your family.

Substance abuse. The physical, emotional and financial strains on the road to becoming a doctor can be overwhelming. Long hours studying difficult subjects, long years wondering how to pay for the education and a schedule which keeps the young doctor isolated from family creates an environment in which some doctors turn to drugs or alcohol for the quick fix to keep them going. At first it may be occasional, but the pattern often becomes progressive and can eventually dominate the doctor's life, creating even more physical, emotional and financial strains.

While some medical problems can be treated by common sense and a little science, most require considerably more intellect and information. This is difficult enough with the full possession of one's senses, attempting this while under the influence of drugs is a prescription for tragedy. If the doctor has an erratic personality, if there are unexplained absences from the office or if the doctor becomes unavailable without arranging for coverage of the practice, these may be signs of substance abuse. Notifying your local medical society may save other patients from harm and may help the doctor seek treatment before it is too late.

Professional bullying. The professional's job is to guide a patient or client past hazards toward a goal. The professional is supposed to provide expertise to anticipate the hazards and education the patient needs to understand the nature of his undertaking. It is not difficult to dazzle and confuse an unknowing patient with professional jargon and a discussion of science fiction exploits. Patients may temporarily forget the goals and values they have brought to this relationship or may be so intimidated by the professional's performance that they believe their original goals are wrong. This is a perversion of the professional relationship.

Your goals may be wrong, impossible, unrealistic or mistaken but the way a doctor must elicit your collaboration is not to bully you into capitulation but rather to provide education that helps you set your path.

To my mind, the professional's need to control rather than collaborate is a serious deficiency which diminishes the patient. An arrogant physician's great technical expertise will have little value if it is employed to reach the wrong goal. A supersonic jet speeding in the wrong direction takes us further from where we want to go, albeit faster. The implications of serious illness are too great for us to be thrust headlong in the wrong direction. We have to work together to determine your goals, and to achieve them.

The Qualities We Seek

One of my real goals has been to re-emphasize the importance of the relation of patient, family and family doctor. When I meet new people in a social setting and they learn that I am a doctor on the faculty of a world famous medical school, they invariably ask my speciality. I just as invariably answer that I am a primary care practitioner or family doctor.

Thereafter, a period of silent disbelief is followed by an attempt to get me to admit to some other designation. I sometimes feel they think I am being either bashful or deceptive. Our lust for technology has reduced the prestige of family care to a low level. Machinery has a higher status than people. If I am pushed further, I will say that my speciality is the whole person.

The heart, the lungs or the stomach are only so important as they contribute to the whole person, and my speciality is the integration of these systems with the person in whom they are contained.

Never doubt, however, that technical expertise is important in the practice of any art or profession. An artist who has no skill in the application of the brush to canvas will be unable to communicate successfully with an audience. The lawyer who is ignorant of the law cannot advise clients well. Yet technical proficiency with the brush is not sufficient to permit a painter to communicate as an artist. And a knowledge of the law alone will not give a lawyer the grit to secure justice for a client.

Sensitivity and understanding the patient's values do not alone permit the physician to benefit the patient. It is clearly important that the physician be skilled in the science of medicine. Otherwise, the physician is functioning as a caring friend, not as a professional. Yet that science alone, without the tempering influence of the soul, can distort the course of illness as surely as the application of concern without knowledge.

In our search for a guide, what characteristics are most important? Any characteristic is an abstraction and has no more reality apart from the individual doctor than a disease has apart from the individual sick person in whom it may be expressed. Doctors as individuals exhibit their personal characteristics in many different combinations. However we portray the ideal combination of physician qualities, no human is likely to embody them in exact proportion. The ideal physician, just as the ideal spouse, is an abstraction which may guide us in our search. In the end, the success of that search depends on the role we play in the development of the relationship.

Having said all that, the four characteristics that we seek are:

+ intelligence
+ integrity
+ discretion
+ compassion

Intelligence. Clearly, we seek an informed and intelligent physician. Evidence of continuing post graduate education and certification by organizations such as the American Academy of Family Practice or American College of Physicians, among others, provide assurance of the physician's commitment to keeping up with developments in science since medical school and residency.

Not every doctor is in a position to be a teacher or clinical researcher in primary care, but every one of us is obliged to keep current with the evolution of scientific thinking.

Many state and county medical societies have continuing medical education requirements to maintain membership. Learning what those requirements may be in your area and whether your doctor has been able to satisfy them provides additional assurance of physician technical expertise.

Integrity. The issue of physician integrity is as difficult to assess as it is important. The patient's vulnerability at times of illness and dependence on the physician is unequivocal. You need to be assured that:

+ The physician's interest and your interest as a patient are identical.

✦ The physician has no personal financial stake in the advice that is given.

✦ No test or procedure will be recommended for any reason other than your need.

✦ No necessary test or treatment will be withheld because of a financial reward or penalty for the physician.

Integrity is indivisible. Where an error of intelligence or lack of information can be remedied, any lapse of integrity results in tragic destruction of the physician's credibility and effectiveness. The measurement of this attribute requires experience that most patients lack until they may have to depend upon it. The only trait we can measure in these circumstances is the physician's reputation in the community. This is hardly a secure gauge but better than none.

Discretion. Another aspect of the physician's integrity is our trust in his discretion. Only if you have assurance that what you say to the physician will be held in strictest confidence are you likely to reveal those details which may be crucial to effective diagnosis and treatment.

I take care of many adolescent children of adult patients and friends. They all know and depend upon my sincere commitment to confidentiality. Nevertheless, I preface my initial visits with a statement affirming my commitment but reserve the right to call a parent if I believe that the young person is in serious danger of his life, either by his own hand or for some other reason.

In other situations in which a parent will have left a message to call after a visit with her child, I will sometimes call the parent while the young patient is in the office, but only after having secured permission. Short of the issues of immediate life and death, the ability to rely on the absolute discretion of the physician is utterly necessary.

Compassion. The characteristic of compassion has been an underlying premise of this book. Over and over we have emphasized the importance of seeing each person as a complex, frequently unpredictable being. However many numbers we use to describe his functions, those numbers do not describe his soul.

X-rays and scans show us the shadows but miss the essence of a patient. Compassion is taking account of our essential humanity, understanding the hopes, aspirations, fears and despair that are a part of every human being.

Doctorly compassion is not just the concern for fellow man but a recognition of the serious importance of those intangible factors in the course of illness. How you measure your physician against this yardstick before using his services is almost as difficult as gauging his integrity. Short, urgent visits to deal with self-evident problems may limit the time available for your physician to give evidence of his human concern. Yet some time must be allotted to a more general discussion of your health risk factors. It is not possible to be an effective physician without knowing what a patient's family history may be, where he lives, with whom he lives, and what he does for a living.

If your physician is always too busy or uninterested in the fabric of your life, even when you make an appointment in advance, then it is very likely that he is not going to be interested in the topics we've been discussing in this book. He may be an intelligent and honorable person. He may contribute his time and skills to the community in a generous fashion. Nevertheless, when you need an assessment of the options of diagnosis and treatment that lie ahead in the course of serious illness, this doctor is not likely to provide it.

But don't give up too easily. If you have found a doctor available and his advice and treatment have resulted in your improvement, you should be appropriately reluctant to give up without a final chance.

Take notice of how the doctor acts in, say, a situation in which you want to come in and talk about a Living Will or Durable Power of Attorney:

✦ How does the doctor respond when you come in for an appointment?

✦ Does he acknowledge your concerns and make sure you are scheduled at a time when your questions can be answered fully without the intrusions of other demands?

✦ Does he have sample forms or literature on the subjects that you can read ahead of time?

✦ If he doesn't have them in the office, does the receptionist have a list of references that you can get at the public library?

✦ Are you dismissed with, "Why do you want to worry about that now?"

This is a relevant test because you are preparing for needs that are part of everyone's future. If the doctor flunks this one, find another doctor.

The danger is unfortunately high that at some point you will be very sick and every blood test and x-ray will be run on you, but your suffering will be unrelieved.

The Role of a Family Doctor

The obvious roles of diagnosis, making a judgment about what may be wrong with you, and treatment define the general activity of medicine. These roles can be played by any physician, whether in an emergency room or working temporarily in a free-standing urgent care clinic.

The role of a real family doctor requires more personal commitment, both in terms of length and depth of service.

The expectation of continuity means an interest in preventing problems of the future, not just solving the problems of today.

Search for underlying causes. The concern with depth of service is another aspect of the commitment to continuity. It means looking for root causes, both physical and behavioral, which may produce today's disease. The doctor should discuss, for example, the way cigarette smoking predisposes a person to the development of acute bronchitis—not just prescribe an antibiotic to treat this instance.

Education of patient. The type of health education the doctor can provide will vary with each patient and the type of problem presented. If the nature of the doctor's practice is such that he cannot deliver all of the education himself, does he have a nurse or assistant to whom he will refer you for follow-up? Issues of cigarette smoking, alcohol misuse, dietary guidance, parenting and sexual diseases are among the concerns addressed under a physician's direction. While many of the education issues are general, there are some which may be specific to people with certain family histories, occupations or lifestyles. Does the doctor sit down at some time to review with the patient what his particular health risks may be, so that these risks can be more personally addressed?

The doctor needs to explain in an understandable way what he believes to be the matter with the patient and the various treatment options, which includes doing nothing. He also needs to point out the areas in which only you can effect a change.

The power of education is greater than the power of drugs. Prevention is much more effective than cure.

Consideration of personal values. The diagnosis and treatment of most serious illness will require the assistance at some point of specialists and hospitals. The family doctor not only helps you see the right ones but guards your personal values when you may be propelled in a direction you don't want to go. He is your advocate both to advance your case and to protect you from ill-advised intervention. If you want to stop treatment and let nature take its course, or if you have developed new symptoms which are only meaningful to someone who knows your previous responses to illness, your family doctor must be your spokesperson. You can't fight city hall alone and your doctor should be a loud voice in your behalf.

Acting as counselor. It's one of the hardest yet satisfying jobs the family doctor can play. When difficult decisions need to be made and you are undecided, she can help you make that decision, knowing your values and applying the principles of your life to the problem at hand. She counsels your family as well. When bad news may have to be told and you don't know how to tell it, she can help. And finally, when complications may develop and life winds down, she remains after the specialists have left.

Educator, advocate, counselor—these are all special roles the family doctor must play, as well as diagnose illness and dispense treatment.

The family doctor values your humanity apart from any disease you may present and is aware of the fallibility that his own humanity confers. The collaboration of doctor and patient together in the struggle to relieve suffering is the crux of medical engagement. If we have been able to identify our goals and find a guide to share the road, then the dark path of illness is no longer lonely. There will always be a light ahead.

You may want to remember:

The four basic characteristics of a good doctor are:
✦ intelligence
✦ integrity
✦ discretion
✦ compassion

You want your family doctor to be someone who:
✦ Searches for underlying causes
✦ Wants to and takes the time to educate you
✦ Considers your personal values
✦ Acts as a counselor

CHAPTER TWELVE

Learning How To Protect Yourself

The treatment of sudden or critical illness often takes place in the hospital. Despite the care we may take in choosing our physician, sudden illness may find us in a different part of town or a different state, where the ambulance takes us to an unfamiliar hospital.

Even if you are fortunate enough to be taken to a hospital where your doctor practices, once admitted you may wind up in an area of the hospital in which he has limited authority. This is often true in specialized cardiac or intensive care units which are run by particular specialists. If you find yourself in this position, what can you do?

Well, if you are awake you can insist on an explanation before signing a consent for any medical procedure or surgery. If you are unconscious, how will your wishes be followed? Will you be subjected to treatments contrary to your wishes because the doctors believe they know best or because they are afraid not to? Your family doctor may be powerless to intervene. He has no legal standing to interpret your wishes without more formal authorization, and you may be unconscious. Anything he says carries little more weight than friendly conversation.

This kind of situation is as likely to happen to a young person in an unpredicted motor vehicle accident as in an elderly person suffering the expected final complication of a long illness. The only way to avoid the possibility of an unknown stranger making life choices for you is to take the trouble to look into some legal forms—now.

Securing Your Rights

The two parts of this are the assignment of a Health Care Proxy and the writing of what has been commonly referred to as a Living Will. The form and validity of these two legal forms differs in the several states and the body of law is in such flux that there will undoubtedly be changes to anything that I write now. I would recommend contacting your doctor's office for guidance in obtaining information about proper procedures in your state. Nevertheless it is essential that you understand the differences between the two documents and how each is designed to protect you.

The Health Care Proxy/Durable Power of Attorney

This document specifies another person whom you designate to act for you in health related decisions if you should be incapacitated. Any procedure that would require a signed consent from you, were you well and conscious, could be agreed to on your behalf by your proxy.

One such situation would be the alteration of an operative plan once you were under anesthesia if there were unexpected findings. You undergo surgery to have a gallbladder chronically irritated by gall stones removed but in the course of the surgery, a localized cancer of the pancreas is found, and the surgeon believes your best chance of cure is to extend the operation and remove the cancer at that time. In the absence of an agreement of Health Care Proxy, the surgeon would be very reluctant to subject you to a complicated operation which has never been discussed with you.

The more usual situation in which the Health Care Proxy would be asked to act would be in case the patient has been rendered permanently incapacitated by illness or accident. A heart patient drops dead in the street only to be resuscitated a little too late for any brain function to return. Such a patient could suffer appendicitis or a perforated duodenal ulcer during the time he is treated for his primary heart and brain diseases. What should the doctor do?

Some people feel that all life must be preserved at all times. Others would be horrified at intervening in the natural death that would occur in such circumstances. While the doctor may well have his own feelings about the issue, his feelings do not count.

**Your wishes are the important ones and only your
Health Care Proxy can carry them out for you.**

Your proxy is in the position to sign the operation permit or to tell the surgeon that he will not sign it and there will be no operation.

What happens if you have no Health Care Proxy designated? The doctor and the hospital try to imagine who your closest relative may be. If you are married, it will probably be your spouse. If you are widowed or divorced, some combination of children or brothers and sisters will be sought. The proposal for the emergency intervention will be discussed, and if the family agrees, the operation or procedure will be done.

**In the absence of a Health Care Proxy, your family member
has no more standing than your family doctor to make a
decision in your behalf.**

Furthermore, the hospital and doctor will probably accept a family decision in these circumstances only if it is in accord with the advice that is given. If the family is reluctant and the doctor is insistent, a battle will often ensue. Either side can appeal to the courts for an order either to permit or prohibit the procedure.

Sometimes these court proceedings are decided with your wishes in mind and, just as often, they are not. There is an inherent antagonism between the ways that law and medicine approach problems. As we have discussed, medicine is concerned with individual circumstance and how the patient has by himself responded to his physical and emotional environment during the course of his illness.

The textbook description of a patient's illness may be interesting to learn and may even give us a clue to the possible directions in which that illness may evolve. Nevertheless, the only real concerns are the actual facts of that individual patient. Not only that there is a pneumonia but that it is a particular type of bacterial pneumonia in a 63-year-old divorced man whose immunological defenses have been diminished by alcoholism and poor nutrition resulting from living alone.

All of these facts are concrete realities from which the designation of pneumonia is an abstraction allowing us to talk about illness. It represents a technical shorthand allowing us to categorize different illnesses.

The law has a very different approach. Law seeks to find general principles that can be applied to everyday life. The purity of the abstract principle is the primary focus of the legal mind.

The *individual* circumstances which intrigue the physician hinder the judge in deciding which of several *abstractions* will most closely fit a case.

In law, the general rule has a sanctity greater than the individual case, whereas in medicine the individual patient has a reality greater than the abstraction we refer to as the disease. If one discipline focuses on the general rule and the other focuses on the individual instance, a terrible contradiction will likely result if both approaches are applied to the same problem. But that is exactly what occurs every time a medical problem ends up in a courtroom.

Other problems include simple human failings. Not every judge asked to decide a medical issue will be equally well versed in understanding the scientific questions at issue. In the technical jargon with which the issue is presented he may easily miss the point of the argument. The judge may be concerned about his record of reversals from higher courts and err on the side of making a decision which is less likely to be reversed than one which will more accurately reflect the wishes of the patient. In a system in which judges are elected to office, the judge may wish not to make a decision which will create media notoriety which could potentially alienate voters.

Obviously, your wishes are more likely to be carried out if you are able to steer clear of the courtroom. No stranger will have your interests at heart with the same intensity as those who know and love you. Be sure they have a chance to help you by making the designation of a Health Care Proxy or Durable Power of Attorney.

The decision of whom to designate as Health Care Proxy may be difficult. It is not a popularity contest. It is not just the person who has known you the longest. As we shall see, there may be many unpleasant duties associated with this designation, and you will want to choose someone whom you can trust to follow your wishes.

Occasionally, I advise patients to choose someone other than their spouse. If the time comes that a decision must be considered to discontinue all treatment and accept the inevitable winding down of life toward death, a spouse will sometimes be unable to follow the patient's instructions to discontinue treatment. Not only does the choice of the spouse in these circumstances hinder the realization of the patient's wishes, but it may leave the spouse with terrible guilt. A spouse may be tormented by the thought that your instructions were not followed, or if your instructions are followed, that he or she had a contributory role in your death.

It goes without saying that the person designated needs to be of unquestioned integrity.

You must be absolutely sure that the person you designate will have only your interest as the agenda.

You cannot worry that the Health Care Proxy will use the occasion of your illness to prematurely hasten your death. Most close friends and family members are able to balance any prospect of gain as an heir or business associate against their sense of personal loss. Some may not be, particularly if an acute financial crisis develops. If this occurs you may be wise to change your proxy. Not only will you be more sure that your wishes will be the first priority, but you will protect your friend from future torment that he might have betrayed, whether or not he did.

GERTRUDE'S NEW PROXIES

"I don't want anybody to pull the plug on me! I want to be sure they leave the plug in. I don't think my son would pull the plug too soon, but his wife would do it as soon as I closed my eyes for a nap. That's why I didn't sign that form that he wanted me to."

Gertrude bristled as the words burst from this otherwise frail little lady. I had asked her what provisions she had made to appoint a Health Care Proxy and whether she had written her wishes in a Living Will. Although her son is a prominent lawyer, I usually offer to meet with patients and their proxies so that we all understand our roles and the patient's wishes. The violence of her reply set me back for a moment, although as I thought about it my surprise diminished.

Gertrude was now frail and 77 years old. She had been a moderately celebrated artist in the past and while she still talked of her studio, she hadn't been there in some time. She had been widowed 10 years before and since lived on her modest savings and her husband's social security. She had only one child, a married son who lived only three blocks away with his wife and two sons.

There had been frequent times over the years when Gertrude had complained that as devoted as she was to her son and however much he professed to love her, her daughter-in-law never spoke to her. She would go on a weekly visit to have dinner and see her grandsons and would make occasional excursions to their house in the country. Yet she claimed that although she would address the woman, she had only once received a reply— and a threatening one at that.

Difficulties between mothers-in-law and daughters-in-law are not new. I have heard complaints from both over the years. The grievances are often related with great hyperbole. When I have known or taken care of both parties, it has been intriguing to see how different-ly each views the same relationship.

Unfortunately, I did not know and would be unlikely ever to meet Gertrude's daughter-in-law. My only view of this relationship was going to be from Gertrude's end of the telescope. Since this relationship had clearly settled into its own rut, there was little more to do than make sympathetic clucking noises when the occasion arose. Never had it occurred to me how this relationship would distort my efforts to help Gertrude plan ahead for medical difficulties.

There was little to be gained from attempting to dis-cuss this with her son. Whenever she tried, he made it very clear that he would brook no interference in his marriage, however well-meaning, even from his mother. This quandary seemed without resolution until I remembered that the grandsons who were 14 and 16 when I first met Gertrude were now 25 and 27. When I suggested that she might consider appointing her grandsons as health care proxies, she brightened immediately.

"That's a great idea. They love me a lot and they would never let their mother pull the plug on me. I am so happy you thought of it. That's the answer."

Admittedly, most people don't have Gertrude's worry, real or imagined, about being a victim of foul play. Yet her problem illus-trates that the solution to any serious question deserves serious thought. Rather than becoming victims, some people instruct their health care proxies to authorize euthanasia, or so-called mercy killing, if they should be in an irretrievable state without hope of recovery to normal life.

This is not possible either. The Health Care Proxy is valid only for legal actions. You cannot require a proxy to perform an illegal act in your behalf, whether fraud or homicide. In fact, putting such a request in the document might conceivably invalidate it.

The Living Will

The better place for the expression of your philosophical beliefs is the Living Will. Whereas the Health Care Proxy appoints someone to act in your behalf if you are incapacitated, a Living Will states what you actually want done. The evolution of this separation appears to have resulted from the specific forms in which the Health Care Proxy must be written to comply with various state laws.

These prescribed forms did not always easily allow the inclusion of the kind of information that the person signing it might have wanted included. In addition, when these forms were first used there was not as secure a body of law validating the scope of the Health Care Proxy. The Living Will was written in the hope that it would exert a moral pressure on any court or administrator who might be called upon to make a decision about the writer's course of treatment.

As a clear and considered statement of the patient's values and wishes when still healthy and not under the influence of drugs or pain, the Living Will speaks when the patient no longer can.

The heath care proxy has equal force whether the patient's incapacitation is temporary or permanent. It can be useful in making decisions in the patient's interest while he may be under anesthesia for a curable condition, or in a temporary diabetic coma from which there would be every expectation of recovery.

However, it has more general use when the incapacitation is permanent as in the consequences of a devastating accident or progressive disease. The Living Will basically comes into play as a statement of the patient's feelings about life and death. The usual attitude which encourages its writing is the desire to prevent unnecessary medical interventions if there is no reasonable chance of recovery.

The typical preface states that the patient accepts death as the normal resolution of life, and if life has ebbed to the point that recovery is not possible, then he wishes that his dying not be artificially prolonged. Nevertheless, the Living Will expresses the patient's feelings about the end of life and there is no reason why it cannot be used to urge every possible treatment no matter how unlikely to succeed.

There are five basic types of medical intervention that are discussed in a Living Will:

+ resuscitation
+ surgery
+ pain relief
+ life support
+ nutrition and hydration

Each represents a somewhat different issue and a specific comment should be made about each. In fact, in New York State if a specific comment is not made about nutrition in both the Health Care Proxy and the Living Will, it is presumed that the patient expects nutrition and hydration to be continued even if all else is discontinued.

Resuscitation. It is the attempt to restart the heart after it has stopped. In a frail elderly person, it can be a brutal procedure in which ribs are broken as sufficient force is applied to the breast bone to squeeze blood through the heart. If the patient's heart has stopped as an expected consequence of a progressive and incurable disease, restarting it will not be successful for very long.

It is obviously a very different situation if the heart stops unexpectedly in an otherwise healthy person as a reaction to medication or surgery. It is also a different situation when the heart stops as a consequence of abnormal but temporary electrical activity in a person with a recent heart attack. These are treatable circumstances which can be remedied after the heart has been restarted. No one is advocating the discontinuing of all cardiac resuscitation. Yet to subject a dying patient to the physical and electrical assault of cardiopulmonary resuscitation (CPR) when the heart stoppage is a normal consequence of the illness is cruel.

Resuscitation is the issue about which people will most easily agree. It comes into play at the very end of a progressive illness. It is an active intervention that need not begin.

The failure to start a treatment is emotionally easier to accept than either stopping a treatment already started or an active intervention which may result in death as a side effect.

Sins of omission are usually more tolerable to us than sins of commission.

Surgery. It has many of the same features as resuscitation. We are talking about operating for a bleeding ulcer in a permanently comatose patient or for a blood clot in the leg of a patient with advanced Alzheimers Disease. Again the failure to perform surgery is the failure to undertake a potentially hazardous procedure in a patient whose life will not be substantially improved by the intervention. By specifying in the Living Will that no surgery should be consented to unless it would result in a reversal of the patient's primary disease, you can guard against the unnecessary prolongation of dying.

Pain relief. Analgesia is the medical name for it. The progression of many diseases can result in severe pain. In the past, and unfortunately for some in the present, there have been physicians who have withheld adequate amounts of pain medicines for the wrong reasons. They have been afraid that using large enough doses of narcotics to adequately relieve pain would result in the patient's addiction to the narcotic.

While it is true that the body can become habituated to narcotics in a manner that often requires a definite increase in the amount of medicine required, this is not addiction. A diabetic is not addicted to insulin because he may require increasing amounts. Nor is the hypertensive who needs more medicine to control his blood pressure. Adequate pain relief is an important factor in medical treatment at all stages of illness, but most certainly at the end.

Another common justification for withholding needed pain relief is that the amount of medicine required would accelerate the patient's death. If we are treating a remediable illness, administering a drug which might kill the patient would be stupid. You would not struggle to reverse an illness on the one hand and then give a medication which would undo your efforts.

This is a more complicated situation than simply refraining from initiating treatment as in resuscitation or surgery. This is an active treatment with a clear side effect. However, we are discussing patients with progressive illnesses that are beyond recovery. There is no likelihood that the patient will recover. Why prolong the dying while asking the patient to endure more suffering? Stating that you value a pain-free and gentle death rather than extending the period of dying should make your priorities clear.

Life support. This generally refers to the use of machines to support a patient's breathing. It may be required if a patient is in a deep coma from brain damage. There are other patients with far advanced emphysema who may be placed on a respirator during the course of an acute infection. Some will not have sufficient breathing capacity on their own to be removed from the machine. This device can result in a true living death.

If conscious, the patient is unable to speak because of the tube in his throat. This same tube is irritating and can induce severe coughing as if "something went down the wrong way," particularly when mucus and secretions have to be suctioned by introducing yet another tube. Often sedation has to be administered so that the patient will not fight the machine.

With modern techniques, this situation can be maintained almost indefinitely. A similar situation occurs with other common machine support of life—dialysis for kidney failure. While many people are supported for long periods of productive life, others are placed on dialysis as a futile attempt to stave off death without ever advancing life. To call a halt involves a somewhat different issue than the ones we have considered before.

Doctors have often been reluctant to disconnect a respirator. This is a situation that has sparked a great deal of controversy. It seems too much like actively causing the death of the patient. The close time between the physician's act and the patient's death make the connection inescapable. For a professional usually committed to prolonging life, this is a very uncomfortable role. It is the performance of an active enterprise. And yet, if the physician's primary role is the relief of suffering, this action clearly relieves suffering. The cause of death is not the removal of the respirator so much as it is the disease for which the respirator was initially connected.

If you or I were placed on a respirator and it was then removed, we would live just fine, certainly a lot more comfortably. We have no underlying diseases. It is the underlying brain damage or the emphysema which has been the cause of the patient's death.

By keeping a respirator connected we can sometimes hold off death, but that is not really the same as extending life.

Disconnecting the respirator has been the focus of a large body of public health law over the last two decades. Many of the issues have been discussed in great detail in the press and on television. This discussion has resulted in securing the rights of patients to self-determination. This is an area in which the clear statement of the patient before he becomes ill has the deciding influence.

In some states, the Health Care Proxy or Durable Power of Attorney will, without further specification, allow the turning off of the respirator in hopeless situations. Nevertheless, do not depend on this. Be specific in the Living Will about your wishes. If you are clear, there can be no misinterpretation of your intentions.

Furthermore, the psychological burden for your proxy will be considerably diminished if you spell out your wishes exactly. There will be no agonizing on his part, worried about your intentions and sad that he should have to play a role in your death.

Less uncertainty means less unnecessary delay in carrying out your wishes.

On the other hand if you feel you are against any active intervention that may be the proximate cause of death, state that view in your Living Will or you may find someone else making the decision for you.

Nutrition and hydration. The final issue to be considered is administering of nutrition and hydration. This means, do you want to be maintained with tubes—through your nose, through the abdominal wall, or intravenously, if there is no hope of recovery?

This is a controversial legal point because some courts have interpreted tube feeding as ordinary support of life and not a medical procedure. Therefore they have held that tubal feeding is not as extraordinary an intervention to sustain life as a respirator. New York State, at the time of this writing, requires some statement from the patient specifically mentioning artificial hydration and nutrition. If there is no such statement, the Health Care Proxy will not be presumed to include the withdrawal of this level of support.

Curiously, the rule only requires the patient to assert that he has discussed the issue with his proxy but does not require him to state his specific wishes in the document. Take no chances. Let no no one mistake your wishes.

If the prospect of years of unconscious existence maintained by a tube through your nose horrifies you, say so clearly in both the Living Will and Health Care Proxy.

These topics may appear dreadful, but far more dreadful is the leaving of these important decisions to strangers. The mobility of our population, the technological virtuosity of so much medical intervention and the necessity for poor urban dwellers to rely on hospital emergency rooms for basic care have all resulted in a great dependence on institutions as the source of medical treatment.

The Presumption of Consent

The obvious result is that so many people are treated by physicians who do not know them. Patients come to the hospital in various states of acute suffering. The almost battlefield conditions of urban emergency rooms does not provide an atmosphere for peaceful inquiry into the patient's values and view of life and death.

There is barely enough time to obtain an adequate history of the patient's previous illnesses.

The personnel in the emergency room have to presume that the patients who come or are brought there desire and consent to treatment. They feel obligated, and I believe they are justified, to attack every problem brought to them as vigorously as they can. They will resuscitate, put on life support systems, start hydration and prepare for emergency surgery almost anyone whose medical condition suggests the possibility of benefit.

This presumption of consent and predisposition to action mean that many patients end up with more technological intervention than they might have desired. The patient with a progressive disease beyond medical cure is attacked with the same vigor as the patient who will benefit from the technology.

This situation is compounded by the absence of family physicians who may understand a patient's life and values.

The intensive care unit staff continues the intervention begun in the emergency room and is reluctant to accept the "defeat" that letting the patient go gently may represent to them.

If the patient or his family objects to the intervention, they will often be intimidated by technical jargon and space age machinery. The presumption of doctors, not founded in any true knowledge, is that they are obligated to treat every condition with which they are presented. They fear legal, criminal and media penalties if they do otherwise. This is a fiction of the "technological imperative," the belief that because a treatment is possible, it must be attempted.

The role of the physician is the relief of suffering and when that suffering is increased by inappropriate intervention, the "technological imperative" is negated.

Our discussion of Health Care Proxies and Living Wills should give you the tools to secure your wishes, even if you are no longer in a position to speak for yourself. It is not enough that you think about and sign a Health Care Proxy and Living Will. You need to discuss it with the people involved—particularly your family.

If they merely find the papers in your desk drawer after you are hit by a car, they will still be in too much of a state of shock to know what to do. Just as I am anxious for my patients to think about "end of life" goals while they are still healthy, I want them to bring their family members to the office so that we can all discuss the implications of what they have written.

There are three general areas that I want to review with them:

✦ **Differences between the Health Care Proxy/Durable Power of Attorney and the Living Will.** These interventions and their efficacy, discomfort and extension of life have some frightening possibilities that often scare readers into thinking about something else. The only way to be sure that the message gets through is to repeat it often enough in different ways.

✦ **Ethical Implications.** Most family members come to a meeting with the same belief that the "technological imperative" has some moral force. They seem afraid to stick up for what they believe and need to be told that their human instincts can serve as an important basis for conduct.

✦ **Prolongation of Life vs. Relief of Suffering.** They also have to understand the distinction between the prolongation of life (or the prolongation of dying) and the relief of suffering. Also, the legal aspects of omission of treatment as well as acts of commission, including the exclusion of active euthanasia or assisted suicide.

After we have discussed what the words mean and the ethical implications of the various choices the patient has made, I urge the family and the patient to discuss their emotional reactions to the choices. Not only does the proxy agent have to be sure of what the patient wants, but the patient has to be assured that the agent will be able to follow his requests.

You may want to remember:

✦ We have mentioned the quandary in which some close family members may find themselves if they feel that they are participating in ending the patient's life. If this is going to be a problem, the time to discover it is long before the occasion arises. It is often difficult for family members to talk about these emotionally charged issues together. Having someone guide the discussion will allow them to explore these feelings more successfully.

✦ Another important factor is discovering whether there is any serious disagreement in the family about the choices the patient has made. In extreme cases, it may mean that someone disagrees so strongly that he may seek a court order to prevent the appointed agent from acting. Understanding this early may allow the patient to influence the critic and diffuse the problem.

✦ The family generally seeks assurance that "everything possible" will be done. This assurance is sought at the time of theoretical discussion but certainly with even greater intensity when a patient is lying unconscious in the hospital bed.

✦ The way to reconcile any conflict is to, at every moment, do everything possible for the patient. "Everything possible" is just as accurately applied to providing pain relief, medicines to ease nausea or shortness of breath, or surgery to fix a broken hip which will allow the patient to walk to his dining room while he still has the strength.

"Everything possible" does not mean continuing to administer chemotherapy which has already failed to help. It does not mean prolonging the dying with ventilators or dialysis machines when there is no possibility of reversing the underlying disease. Any family deserves the promise that good medicine always depends on doing everything possible, but it is the patient's responsibility to be sure that the provisions for "everything possible" are according to his wishes.

CHAPTER THIRTEEN

Life Winding Down

One advantage to keeping the treatment of serious disease at home is that it keeps private the decisions to be made by patients and families, rather than strangers in authoritarian roles. But how can we keep treatment at home when very sick people need so much? Aren't they better off in the hospital where much more can be done for them? This question faces every family as life winds down. As long as there is a treatment that will retard or eliminate disease at a personal price the patient is willing to pay, the hospital is an appropriate place for treatment.

Yet when the time comes that technological interventions no longer have a useful purpose, what's to be done? Hospitals are places where staff members are focused on cure.

The patient admitted for pain relief and a gentle death is often unconsciously ignored or, worse, subjected to interventions which prolong the dying.

The remedy to this is a service which allows the patient to remain at home where his wishes determine the course of treatment.

Hospice Care

When you remove operating rooms, intensive care units, respirators, diagnostic laboratories and x-ray facilities from the hospital, you are left with a patient in a bed and a doctor and nurse at bedside. There is not a lot of equipment that could not just as well be provided at home. The doctor has to make up a medical plan for pain relief, diet and the treatment of wounds that may interfere with the patient's comfort. The nurse has to make a treatment plan for care of the patient's ordinary bodily needs and for implementation of the doctor's medical orders. The nurse also needs to train and supervise any family members who will be involved in the daily care of the patient, including the administration of medicines which may have been ordered by the doctor.

Treatment and Medicare. The technology of pain relief has come a long way since the man first chewed on the bark of the cinchona tree or the leaves of the cocoa plant. Besides highly effective oral narcotic preparations, including special long-acting formulations and rectally active forms, there are newer preparations which are applied through the skin so that patients unable to swallow or those with intestinal obstructions will not have any interruption in pain relief—or be required to be hospitalized for this reason alone. There are, of course, still injectable preparations, which can give the fastest onset of activity if the need arises.

Treatment for nausea is available by pill, liquid, rectal suppository or injection. Diet formulations can be thinned or thickened depending upon a patient's specific type of swallowing difficulty. Electric hospital beds, portable commodes (toilets), suction devices, walkers, wheelchairs and supplemental oxygen are all readily available for rental in the home. In addition, financial barriers for most patients have been removed since Medicare covers home Hospice services for a full 12 months. However, the coverage of these services by other insurance programs is variable and needs to be examined on an individual basis.

A hospice service is fulfilling its mission if it:

♦ Integrates emotional support into the provision for
the patient's physical needs.
♦ Provides an active program of family education; and

Emotional support of the family. After assuring the patient's comfort, the next most important factor in home hospice care is supporting the family. Mixed with the grief of anticipating the loss of a family member is the very real anxiety about being up to the requirements of caring for him. This is a very scary business for young people who are learning to be doctors and nurses caring for people with whom they do not have a family relationship. The sense of inadequacy becomes even more intensely focused when it is Mother or Grandfather or Aunt Vivian for whose care you have accepted some responsibility.

Often the initial shift in thinking from the search for cure to the emphasis on comfort is the most difficult for the family. It requires them to come to grips with losing someone who is dear to them.

No matter how accepting a patient and family may be, intellectually and emotionally, there is usually a small corner of the spirit that waits for the miracle of recovery.

This is the corner that is most reluctant to give up the siren call of the technological imperative. The magical appeal of that wish can obscure the consideration of today's concrete needs.

This is not being obstinate or uncooperative. It is a normal exhibition of the human quality of ambivalence, discussed in earlier chapters. In any case, this is one of the factors that cause a family to worry about whether everything can be done at home as well as it would be done in the hospital.

What needs to be emphasized is that, in most cases, things can be done much better at home than in the hospital.

At home, the patient is the center of attention, rather than an obstacle to the smooth running of an institution. At home, there is no separation from the family. Rather than being alienated at the time of greatest need, the family is able to express their love in the most immediate and concrete manner. Not only does this give the patient a sense of protection, but it spares individual family members the regret of "tasks never accomplished" when death finally comes.

Family education. After the family's reconciliation with the knowledge that death is inevitable and the recognition that technology as available in the hospital no longer has anything special to offer, the task of family education becomes the next priority.

Learning how to help feed the patient, how to turn him so that a minimum of pain is incurred, how to manage bowel and bladder functions are obvious once observed a few times. Many of the phobic reactions to specific tasks can be dispelled by participating in the treatment. There may be individual instances in which this is *not* true, and serious attention must be paid to this if an adequate treatment program is our goal.

Sometimes families are more comfortable if they have something written to refer to when the supervising nurse is not there. If a particular hospice service does not have an appropriate brochure, I would recommend *Dying at Home: A Family Guide for Caregiving* by Andrea Sankar (Johns Hopkins University Press, 1991). This beautiful book describes in very personal terms the author's own experiences and supplements with examples from others. The patient's families to whom I have recommended it have been grateful for its explicit advice.

A family's pride in being able to provide for the patient's needs usually adds an air of tranquility to the home.

While the work may be long and hard, the resulting satisfactions continue to motivate everyone.

Nevertheless, as life winds down, the fear of what things will be like at the end begin to loom larger. Everyone worries that at the moment of leaving, the patient will have some need to which they will not be equal. Some worry about choking, pain or other possibilities. In an expected death, with adequate pain medication, death is gentle. As the day approaches, the patient will often withdraw from his surroundings and it is not unusual for there to be a reduction in some of the pain medicine required.

There may be noisy breathing and even sounds like moaning, but they do not have the significance of pain expression. Of course, if there is any doubt, more pain medicine can be appropriately given. Sometimes the moment passes and you will not realize for awhile that the breathing has stopped, just like an old grandfather clock that winds down and, all of a sudden, you notice the ticking has stopped. No matter how expected, the flood of emotion at that moment can be overwhelming. Don't fight it. There is nothing more important to be done. Calling others or the funeral director can wait. This is a time for that awesome feeling of peace mixed with extreme sorrow that is a part of no other experience.

Preparing for the Unexpected

Sometimes unexpected things do happen. Not every possibility is always predictable. There are times when the family becomes ill and cannot provide the care it had. Part of home hospice is the recognition that there must be rapid and available backup at all times. Not every crisis demands a home visit. Sometimes being able to talk to someone knowledgeable over the telephone can dispel anxiety.

Still there are times when the patient may not be able to continue to be cared for at home—such as when a new fracture has occurred and the pain can be stabilized better with a short period of hospitalization. The family needs to know that there is always an out. This knowledge gives courage and support when things are bleak.

Knowing that you are not cornered allows you to concentrate on each step as it comes—doing today's work without being paralyzed by tomorrow's fear.

There is another special issue which comes up from time to time. Some families at the very end don't want the patient to die at home. If the patient is beyond suffering and the family is obviously in pain over the decision, I respect their wishes. The difficulty is picking the proper moment to make the transfer, knowing that with admission to a hospital you cannot control every well-intentioned intervention which may inadvertently put off for weeks an expected and peaceful death in a comatose patient.

It is sometimes difficult to weigh the suffering of a family that does not want to remember the living room as the place where Father died, with the suffering which may result from three or four weeks of prolonged dying because of a hospital nurse's compulsion for aggressive treatment.

Each situation has its own solution.
Frequently it remains unknown to even
the most experienced of us.

PHIL'S CANCER

Phil came to see me when he felt a painful swelling under his jaw. He was a cheerful and dapper retired advertising man who lived across the street from me. He took a quick-paced constitutional early every morning and our paths often converged for a few blocks as I walked to the office. While I had been his doctor a long time, I did not see him much. He was never very sick. I got to know him mostly because his wife Nina had had many complicated illnesses until she died of emphysema a few years before.

The swelling under Phil's jaw was stone hard and it seemed to be tender because it had grown so rapidly, stretching the tissues taut around it. The ominous diagnosis proved accurate when the biopsy report showed an aggressive cancer. The swelling continued to enlarge while follow-up tests were done to determine whether there was any possibility of operating for a cure. The scans showed that the swelling had progressed too far for a safe operation and plans were made for a combination approach of chemotherapy and radiotherapy.

The periods of hospitalization for the intense chemotherapy were very debilitating for Phil. I was astonished by how resiliently a man of eighty was still able to bounce back after that medical assault. But bounce back he did, and, to everyone's delight and surprise, the cancer rapidly shrank. The x-ray treatments proved more of a problem because the tissues around the cancer became inflamed. It was several weeks before Phil could swallow comfortably again. He lost a lot of weight during this time but, having been pretty well nourished before the ordeal, he regained the weight quickly after the inflammation subsided.

Several months passed and, at his monthly examinations I noticed that the scarred area where the cancer had been seemed quiet. Then, after about the ninth month, I felt a new bump around the scar. I sent Phil back to the specialist for an examination. He agreed that this was likely to be a recurrence of the cancer. Scans confirmed the opinion and a decision was made to restart the chemotherapy. Unfortunately the treatment had taken its toll on Phil. He didn't bounce back so quickly from the first treatment and the cancer did not regress with the same speed that it had the first time. After the even more devastating second round of chemotherapy, Phil made an appointment to see me in my office.

He was wizened and tired as he sat in the chair next to my desk. His voice was weaker than it had been. "Dr. John," he started, "I've had enough. The treatments worked so well the first time that I felt I could put up with the side effects. Now, I am much weaker and the treatments are really not working at all. Dr. Walker has been calling me. He wants me back in the hospital for another round, but I just can't take it. I know I am not going to live forever, and I don't want to spend the last days of my life vomiting in the hospital. Can you help me?"

*SOUL*MEDICINE

Phil had given me his Living Will some years before and we had talked then about his wish for a gentle end to life. As we talked now he re-iterated those wishes and the desire to remain at home at the end. He was close to his sons but only one lived in New York. The other lived in California. He did not have full-time help and there would clearly be some problems as his needs became greater. I went over the medical issues he might face and told him there was no unusual problem that would prevent him from being treated at home. At the end of the visit he asked me to call Dr. Walker and tell him that he had appreciated his help but he wasn't planning on going back into the hospital again.

A few weeks later, Phil called and asked me to come to his house. He didn't feel strong enough to go out any longer. When I arrived, his son was there and we talked about the kind of help Phil would need and how to provide it. This was several years ago when the hospice movement was in its infancy in New York. I had no sense of the services available and did not recommend any. Fortunately, after our meeting, Phil's daughter-in-law Mary searched further.

Mary found a small hospice program based at a downtown hospital and asked if I would be willing to work with them. I was delighted. The Medicare regulations had recently been changed to pay for comprehensive hospice care and the list of services available was extensive. The program would provide all the medications required by the patient and arrange for their delivery. A visiting nurse would come as often as necessary to both supervise the medical situation or counsel the family. Any other equipment, hospital beds, walkers, wheelchairs or suction devices would be available as well. If the patient's doctor was not willing or able to play a role in the care, the program would supply a supervising doctor as well. The family, however, did have to provide the basic daily care, either themselves or by providing someone else in the home.

At first, most of the daily care was performed by Ellen, a practical nurse who had taken care of Nina, Phil's wife, before she had died. She was familiar with their home and she and Phil had gotten along very well during those difficult days. Having a familiar face and someone whose experience had been tested reduced the anxiety that everyone felt embarking on this critical adventure.

The tumor began to grow more rapidly and swallowing became more difficult. Solid foods were out and only pureed meals were possible. The combination of the reduced food intake and the metabolic needs of the tumor produced an even more rapid weight loss and increasing weakness in Phil. Phil's son from California came and spent a week caring for his father. The closeness of the family was rekindled as everyone realized how quickly Phil was failing. Phil was spending more time sleeping both because of the amount of pain medicine he required and from his weakness. We got a suction machine for him to use when it became too difficult for him swallow his saliva.

I visited frequently to adjust medication and to help the family understand the processes going on. The question of how long this might continue had important significance since Phil's California son wanted to spend as much time as possible with him but also had a job and responsibilities 3,000 miles away. It was no easier predicting time for Phil than it had been for my mother, and the uncertainty produced a greater sense of urgency for everyone.

Finally, Phil seemed to go into a sort of trance. He stopped taking food but he would take some water from time to time. He began talking to people only he could see and appeared to enjoy their company very much. He stopped asking for pain medicine and seemed quite comfortable without it. He stopped talking and lapsed into coma. His breathing became noisy and erratic and then it stopped too. His sons were with him, and, after a while, they called to tell me. I came over to write out the death certificate.

Another long struggle was over but another person had achieved a gentle death with a family which will always treasure the closeness they achieved supporting each other.

Not every patient and every family have the personnel or emotional abilities to manage home hospice. There are lots of situations where some other arrangement will be necessary.

Disabling illness can tax the physical and emotional resources of any family. Strokes, severe arthritis, deteriorating diseases of the brain and of the nervous system are among these. However much the patient and his family may wish to maintain treatment at home, it may not be possible. This is the time when you have to consider other alternatives.

The Nursing Home Alternative

Many nursing homes have acquired a well deserved reputation as hell holes—places where rapacious owners prey on ignorant and demented patients without families, provide substandard care and underpay their employees. However, this is not universally the case and there are things that you can do to improve your chances.

Visit possible nursing home choices yourself—more than once. Try, if you can, to visit when you are not expected. This can be difficult if you do not know any other patients at that particular home, but you can be creative and claim that you were in the neighborhood and wanted another look for such an important decision.

Ask among friends and associates about others who may have experience with particular places. Obviously the family doctor may have had other patients there and can give you a better evaluation; or your clergyman may have paid visits and formed an opinion about the staff.

Try to find out who owns the nursing home and for how long. Is it owned by a philanthropic organization or an individual?

Is this a long-term commitment to the care of the infirm with a commendable track record or a new investment by inexperienced people who seek to reap a financial windfall?

Asking visitors in the parking lot or people aleaving the nursing home can result in more candid opinions.

The job does not end when you have chosen a nursing home. The best way of eliciting the concern of the staff is to show your concern. If you and your family are there often, the staff will get the idea that not only is the patient a valued person but that there are people around who will be alert to any diminution of service. As I have said before, the squeaky wheel gets the oil. When the patient cannot squeak, you have to squeak for him. The carrot and stick approach is also effective. You provide an incentive and demonstrate cooperation while also making clear the standard of care that you expect to have delivered.

Not all nursing home admissions are for life. Some people will demonstrate substantial and often unexpected improvement. Perhaps the experience of watching the care that has been necessary in the nursing home may give you courage to try it at home. Or other circumstances will change to allow the extra effort which may be necessary to maintain the patient at home.

Sometimes the sadness you may feel having your parent or spouse go into a nursing home can be tempered by the hope that he or she may be one of those who are discharged. This is even true in a nursing home devoted to the terminal care of cancer patients. The director of one such place in New York told me that as many as one out of ten patients is discharged to be cared for at home before being re-admitted for their final days.

Our discussion of the gentle end of life often leads to the question of euthanasia or physician-induced death at the patient's request. There are many hideous deaths. During the course of successful treatments there are times when normal people may cry out to be allowed to die. Many physicians struggle with the question of whether it is right to relieve suffering by causing a patient's death or whether the giving of medicine to terminate life is immoral. Drs. Kevorkian and Quill are two cases in point. Dr. Kevorkian is a retired pathologist who has traveled to several states to relieve people of their lives. Dr. Quill, an oncologist, wrote about helping one of his long-term patients to die after a prolonged course of leukemia.

I do not think doctors should be in the business of killing people. I think it represents a conflict of interest. It is often hard work to relieve suffering. It takes creative imagination to understand the nature and cause of the suffering and to devise a plan to relieve it.

If, when stuck with a difficult problem, one choice is to dispense with the problem, I may be less motivated to work at a better solution. Rarely do patients give up all hope. We've discussed Nina, who had excruciating pain from pancreatic cancer. She wanted to die to relieve her suffering. When we relieved her suffering by a different means, she no longer wanted to die. She was grateful for the relief and for the extra time it afforded her with her family.

What of the nagging old person without a family who says he wants to die? Do we decide to accede to the wish, noting that it will save money and relieve ourselves of the necessity to hear the implied rebuke in the daily litany of complaints that we may be unable to improve? If we have the right to end patients' lives and they know it, how will that affect the collaborative relationship between doctor and patient? Will patients be afraid that if they displease us we will kill them as punishment?

I am opposed to suffering. It is my primary job to relieve it. There are few medicines that I would fail to use if I thought they would relieve a patient's suffering. But the primary motivation is the relief of suffering not the termination of life.

I think that what Dr. Kevorkian is doing is shameful. He is not being a doctor. He has no real doctor-patient relationship with the people whose life he helps end. I worry that some of the people who have sought his help do not have terminal illness. He is not counseling them on alternative methods of relieving their suffering. He couldn't, even if he chose to. He has been trained as a pathologist. He is an expert in the examination of tissues and body fluids in the laboratory. He has not devoted his professional life to learning the cause and relief of human suffering. How dare he so demean the work of thousands of primary care doctors and many specialists who have sat holding their patients' hands to communicate human concern of one person for another after the brilliance of technology has dimmed.

Sticking a needle in someone's vein and showing them how to start the flow of poison down the tubing into their bodies does not qualify in my mind as a humane approach to the relief of suffering.

Dr. Quill's experience is very different. He had a long professional relationship with his patient and her family. He had many discussions over a long period of time with the patient and sought to counsel her and review alternatives with her at a time when she understood her options. Only then did he accede to her request as an honorable extension of his treatment of her.

I do not know if I would have done the same. I was not there. But I do not criticize Dr. Quill. He agonized and suffered over his decision as a real physician would and the practice of medicine is often too personal an expression of the particular path of a single patient and physician to be judged by others.

There is another fundamental difference between the approaches of Dr. Kevorkian and Dr. Quill. It may seem unimportant to distinguish between a lethal injection and a lethal prescription, but there are serious differences.

The lethal injection requires the physician to be present to initiate the intravenous route. There may be a certain intimidation value in having caused all this equipment to be assembled which might impel the patient to continue even if some doubts arise.

A lethal prescription preserves patient autonomy. The patient may elect to fill the prescription or keep it as an option for the future. The patient may indeed fill the prescription but not take it, gaining a certain relief from knowing that if things got worse there would be an avenue of escape. That time of escape is always to be determined by the patient not the convenience or schedule of the doctor. If the patient at the last moment wants to think about it more, there is no urgency to speed things along. The patient remains in control. Furthermore, the physician can continue to actively seek the relief of suffering by other means, even after the lethal prescription has been written.

There is the argument that a patient may reach a point at which he will lose either the physical or intellectual capacity to cause his own death, and he will prefer to do it ahead of time on his own schedule. This is an occasional concern but one that can usually be prepared for by Living Will and/or Health Care Proxy provisions. However skilled a doctor, we cannot predict with certainty the time table of a patient's decline. To act to end a life prematurely on the basis of such uncertain judgment is foolish. I cannot tell a patient suffering from moderate arthritis of the hip how long it will take him to progress to the point of such disability that he may need a hip replacement. People and their diseases progress at their own pace.

What may be a reasonable prediction as a general rule may not be accurate for that particular person. How much more terrible to pretend certainty when predicting the variable course of multiple sclerosis or ALS or Alzheimer's disease.

The reliance of the patient upon the supposed inevitability of the future may frighten him into acts which do not accurately reflect his values or the realities of human error.

No general rule can cover all specific circumstances. Yet, the prohibition against physician-induced death will serve to strengthen patient-physician collaboration in the struggle against suffering. The rare case in which the benefit from physician-assisted euthanasia would significantly reduce suffering is substantially overwhelmed by the trust that patients now have that their physician will not knowingly harm them.

While we all seek a gentle end, the human capacity for hope will most often endeavor to delay even the gentlest until our last satisfaction has been wrung from life.

When my mother was dying, I was unaware of the home hospice services available and we were fortunate in having been able to manage well without them. Phil and his family benefited greatly from the services provided by the hospice program. I would not advise others to try this path alone when help is available.

The first source of information should be your family doctor. If he does not have the information, or if you do not have a family doctor on whom to rely, do not wait for hospital staff or specialists to make the suggestion. Contact the National Hospice Organization in Arlington, Virginia for the names of organizations in your area that can help. This is too important an issue to leave to strangers.

When we have done all we could, the sadness of our losses
will be tempered by the beautiful memories in our hearts
of the time we allowed the patient in our family to
wind down life gently and die precisely as requested.